Extra

# History

## Resources & Revision

### Junior Certificate

Patsy McCaughey

Mentor Books Ltd.,
43 Furze Road
Sandyford Industrial Estate
Dublin 18
Republic of Ireland

Tel: +353 1 295 2112/3 Fax: +353 1 295 2114
e-mail: admin@mentorbooks.ie
www.mentorbooks.ie

A catalogue record for this book is available from the British Library



The paper used in this book is made from the wood pulp of managed forests. For every tree felled, at least one tree is planted, thereby renewing natural resources.

ISBN: 978-1-906623-49-4

Cover: Mary Byrne
Cover Image of Robert Emmet and Henry Joy McCracken:
Courtesy of the National Library of Ireland
Typesetting and layout: Kathryn O'Sullivan and Mary Byrne
Editor: Treasa O'Mahony

**3 5 7 9 10 8 6 4**

## YEAR 1

# YEAR 2

# YEAR 3

# Revision Summaries

# Acknowledgements

The Publishers would like to thank:

AKG Images; Alamy; Bridgeman Art Library; Corbis; Jamil Dar; Terry Fagan, Director of the Dublin North Inner City Folklore Project; John Frost newspapers; Getty Images; Clive Limpkin; *National Geographic*; National Library of Ireland; Michael Phillips; *The Irish Times*; Ulster Museum.

The Publishers have made every effort to trace and acknowledge the holders of copyright for material used in the book. In the event of a copyright holder having been omitted, the Publishers will come to a suitable arrangement at the first opportunity.

# WHAT IS HISTORY?

Question 1: PICTURES

## (a) Picture A

**Examine Picture A and answer the questions that follow:**

(i) State what particular task archaeologist A is doing.

(ii) What other job might any of the other archaeologists be doing?

(iii) Name two archaeological tools that are being used at this dig.

(iv) List two other tools that would be used at an archaeological dig.

(v) Name two different ways in which an archaeologist could date any artefacts that are found at this dig.

## (b) Picture B

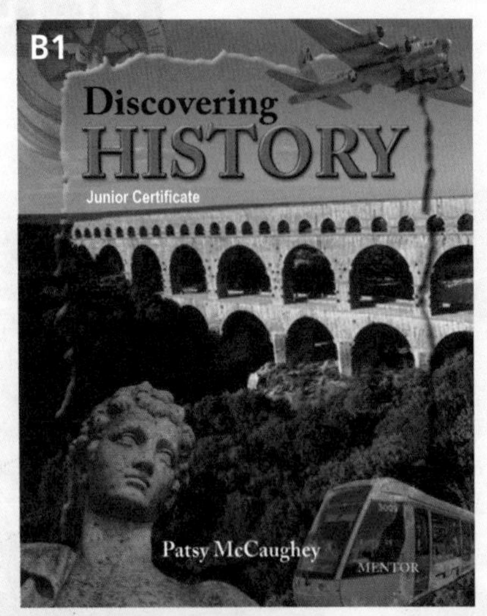

**Examine the different sources in the pictures B1, B2, B3 and B4 and answer the questions below.**

(i) Examine B1, B2, B3 and B4 and state if they are primary or secondary sources.

(ii) Explain how a newspaper from a particular day could be both a primary and a secondary source.

(iii) Explain the differences between a primary source and a secondary source.

(iv) Why is it easier to find sources from more recent events than ancient events?

## Question 2: DOCUMENTS

Study Documents **1a, 1b** and **2** and then answer the questions that follow.

**(a)**

### Document 1a

This is a quote from Thierry Henry, captain of the French soccer team, after he 'handled' the ball in a 2010 World Cup qualifying match between France and Ireland.

*I have said at the time and I will say again that yes I handled the ball. I am not a cheat and never have been. It was an instinctive reaction to a ball that was coming extremely fast in a crowded penalty area. . . . It is impossible to be anything other than that.*

### Document 1b

This is a quote from Robbie Keane, captain of the Republic of Ireland soccer team, after the World Cup match.

***Henry nearly caught it, so it's a bit of a killer. When you see the reaction of the players, Shay [Given – the Irish goalkeeper] especially, he's two yards away from it and you don't get a reaction like that if he's not sure it's a handball. He almost caught it and ran into the net with it. Henry is a top player and has been for a long time but it was a clear handball. He dragged it in from going out. He nearly caught it. I wouldn't expect it from anyone.***

**Read the two Documents, 1a and 1b, of the same event.**

(i) Examine the sources above and state if they are primary or secondary sources.

(ii) From the above statements, does Thierry Henry believe he has cheated? Give a reason for your answer.

(iii) Give one difference between the two accounts of the events.

robbies point of view

(iv) Give an example of how Robbie Keane's account is subjective.

(v) Do you think that Robbie Keane believes Henry cheated? Give a reason for your answer.

(vi) From your reading of Robbie Keane's account of the goal, do you think he is pleased or not? Give evidence to support your answer.

## (b) Document 2

THE Sun

Tuesday, May 4, 1982 14p TODAY'S TV: PAGE 12

QE2 IS SET TO SAIL FOR WAR

Liner may be turned back from a cruise

We told you first

# GOTCHA

SUNK

Our lads sink gunboat and hole cruiser

# Gotcha!

**Our lads sink Gunboat and hole cruiser.**

**The Navy had the Argies on their knees last night after a devastating double punch.**

**WALLOP: They torpedoed the 14,000-ton Argentina cruiser General Belgrano and left it a useless wreck.**

**WALLOP: Task force helicopters sank one Argentine patrol boat and severely damaged another.**

**The Belgrano, which survived the Pearl Harbour attack when it belonged to the U.S. Navy, had been asking for trouble all day.**

**The cruiser, second largest in the Argy fleet, had been skirting the 200-mile war zone that Britain has set up around the Falkland Islands.**

**Examine the cover of *The Sun* newspaper from 1982 during the Falklands war between Argentina and Britain. Then read the extract from the article and answer the questions:**

(i) Give two examples of bias in the article.

(ii) Is this article subjective or objective? Give reasons for your answer.

(iii) Do you think that this article is propaganda? Give reasons for your answer.

(iv) Give an example of exaggeration in the article.

## Question 3:
## SHORT-ANSWER QUESTIONS

(a) Explain the following terms:

(i) Primary source
(ii) Secondary source
(iii) Census
(vi) Bias
(v) Artefact
(vi) Propaganda
(vii) Exaggeration
(viii) Chronology
(ix) Stratigraphy
(x) Dendrochronology
(xi) Anno Domini

(b) Give the correct terms for each time period (length of time):

(i) 12 months
(ii) 10 years
(iii) 100 years
(vi) 1,000 years

(c) Fill in the gaps: Rewrite the following sentences and fill in the missing words:

(i) A good historian asks a lot of q___________ .

(ii) Historians learn about history from different s___________ .

(iii) There are two types of s___________ : p___________ s___________ and s___________ s___________ .

(iv) A photograph of an event is an example of a p___________ s___________ .

(v) The government collects information on the population in a c___________ .

(vi) This book is a ___________ source .

(vii) When someone describes the characteristics of a friend so that they appear nicer than they really are, this is called b___________ .

(viii) P___________ is when information or rumours are spread to influence people's views.

(ix) C___________ is the study of time.

(x) AD stands for A___________ D___________ .

(xi) BCE stands for B___________ the C___________ E___________ .

(xii) A___________ look for a___________ in the ground at digs or e___________ .

(xiii) Precious finds and valuable artefacts from a dig are kept in a m___________ .

(xiv) The method of dating an object using the soil level at which it was found is called s___________ .

(xv) It is possible to date an object by measuring its c___________ levels.

## Question 4: PEOPLE IN HISTORY

**Write a paragraph about the work of an archaeologist.**

- **List the tools that are used.**
- **Explain the different methods used to find locations for digs.**
- **Name three methods of dating artefacts.**
- **List the difficulties faced by an archaeologist at a dig.**

## Question 5:

**Read the following text and answer the questions on page 7:**

The police were called to Clonycavan near Dublin in February 2003 after a peat-cutting machine found a dead body. Three months later, another body was found near Croghan, 40 kilometres from Clonycavan. He was missing a head and his lower limbs. It was soon discovered that these men had lived 2,000 years ago and had been preserved in the bog. The following is a news report about what the archaeologists were able to tell from the body:

*Old Croghan man was . . . young - probably in his early to mid 20s - but much taller than his counterpart from 25 miles away.*
*Scientists worked out from the length of his arms that he would have stood around 6ft 6in tall [2.0m].*

*He had been horrifically tortured before death. His nipples had been cut and he had been stabbed in the ribs. A cut on his arm suggested he had tried to defend himself during the attack that ended his life.*
*The young man was later beheaded and dismembered. Hazel ropes were passed through his arms before he was buried in the bog.*

*Food remains in his stomach show that Old Croghan man had eaten milk and cereals before he died. But chemical analysis of his nails showed that he had more meat in his diet than Clonycavan man.*

*This suggests that he died in a colder season than Clonycavan man, when vegetables were more scarce. It may also explain why his remains are better preserved.*

*The researchers used digital technology to reconstruct the distorted* [twisted] *face of Clonycavan man.*

Source: BBC News, 7 January 2006

(a) How did the archaeologists know what height Old Croghan Man was?

(b) How did the man die?

(c) What food did Old Croghan Man eat?

(d) Was Clonycavan Man vegetarian? Give reasons for your answer.

(e) List what different methods of scientific archaeology the scientists used when examining the bodies.

(f) List <u>three</u> different things that a scientist can learn from the remains of a body or skeleton.

# Question 1: PICTURES

## (a) Picture A

(i) What is the name of this type of building?

(ii) Name two functions that this building could be used for.

(iii) Give two locations of these buildings that exist in Ireland.

(iv) Why is the entrance marked at A not at ground level?

(v) Explain the following terms connected to monasteries:

(a) Scriptorium
(b) Oratory
(c) Beehive huts
(d) Refectory

## (b) Picture B

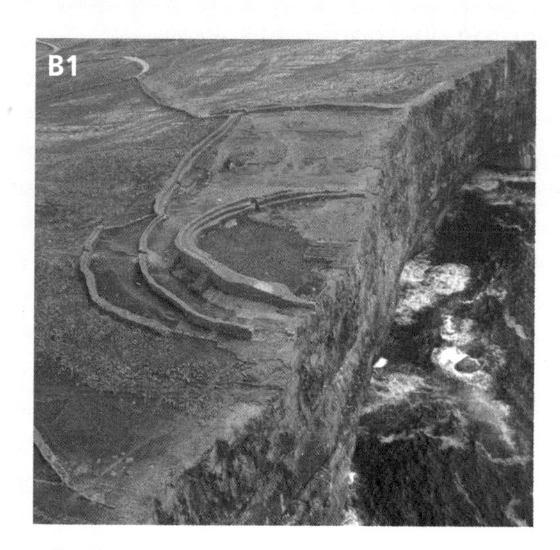

(i) Name the two types of dwellings in B1 and B2.

(ii) Name two locations in Ireland where you might find examples of these types of dwellings.

(iii) From the pictures, what can you tell about the methods of protection that were developed by the Celts during this period. Give two examples from the evidence in B1 and B2.

## (c) Picture C

(i) Name the types of burial tombs in C1, C2, C3 and C4.

(ii) Name the location in Ireland of the tomb marked C3.

(iii) How can burial tombs help archaeologists learn more about the life of ancient Irish civilisations?

(vi) Give two examples of archaeological evidence that an archaeologist might find at a burial tomb from the Stone Age.

## Question 2: DOCUMENTS

Study Documents **1** and **2** below, and then answer the questions that follow.

### (a) Document 1

This is an extract from *Patrick Confessio* (declaration), in *Libri Espistolarum Sancti Patrici Esposcopi*.

My father was the deacon Calpornius, son of the late Potitus, a priest of the town of Banna Venta Berniaw. He had a small estate nearby, where I was taken captive. I was then barely sixteen. I had neglected the true God, and when I was carried off into captivity in Ireland, along with a great number of people it was well deserved. For we cut ourselves off from God and did not keep His commandments, and we disobeyed our bishops who reminded us of our salvation. God revealed His being to us through His wrath [anger]: he scattered us among foreign peoples, even to the end of the earth, where appropriately, I have my own small existence among strangers.

(i) Name St. Patrick's father.

(ii) Where was St. Patrick taken prisoner?

(iii) What age was he when he was taken prisoner?

(iv) Does St. Patrick believe he deserved what happened to him? Give reasons for your answer.

(v) Where was St. Patrick from?

(vi) List two other saints associated with the establishment of monasteries or convents in Ireland.

## (b) Document 2

This is an extract from *Lebor Gabála Erenn,* a collection of poems and prose on the mythical origins of the Irish race from the creation of the world up to the Middle Ages.

> ***Cormac had thrice fifty stewards. There were fifty warriors standing in the king's presence as he sat at his meal. There were three hundred cup-bearers in the fortress, and thrice fifty goblets of carbuncle, of gold and of silver. The total of his household amounted to one thousand and fifty men . . .***
>
> ***Cormac, son of Art the Solitary, was forty years in the kingship of Ireland until he died in Tech Cleitig, after the bone of a salmon stuck in his throat; or it is phantoms that slew him after he had been cursed by Máel-Cenn.***

(i) How many stewards did Cormac have?

(ii) Do you think that Cormac was a wealthy king? Give reasons for your answer.

(iii) For how long was Cormac king of Ireland?

(iv) What are the two ways that the author states could have been the cause of his death?

(v) Did people in ancient Ireland believe in magic and the supernatural? Use evidence from the document to support your answer.

(vi) Name two ancient Irish pagan festivals.

(vii) Outline some of the jobs that a druid would be expected to perform in ancient Ireland.

## Question 3:
## SHORT-ANSWER QUESTIONS

(a) Explain the following terms:

| | | |
|---|---|---|
| (i) Hunter-gatherer | (viii) Monolith | (xv) Brehon |
| (ii) Lunulae | (xi) Aos Dána | (xvi) Filí |
| (iii) Microlith | (x) Crannóg | (xvii) Vellum |
| (vi) Wattle and daub | (xi) Ogham | (xviii) Tánaiste |
| (v) Kerbstone | (xii) Filigree | (xix) Fosses |
| (vi) Smelting | (xiii) Manuscript | (xx) Quill |
| (vii) Fulacht fiadh | (xiv) Bracae | (xxi) Chalice |

(b) Put the periods of the Stone Age in Column A in the correct order and then match them to the correct timespan (a-c) in Column B.

| Column A | Column B |
|---|---|
| 1 Mesolithic | (a) 2,500,000 BC – 8000 BC |
| 2 Neolithic | (b) 8000 BC – 3500 BC |
| 3 Palaeolithic | (c) 3500 BC – 2000 BC |

(c) Fill in the gaps: Rewrite the following sentences and fill in the missing words:

(i) People in the Me________ period of the Stone Age were known as h________-g________.

(ii) M________ hunters used small stones called f________ to make their weapons.

(iii) An example of archaeological evidence of a Mesolithic settlement in Ireland can be found at M______ S______ in County Derry.

(iv) W______ and d______ was a method of making walls in Neolithic huts by placing mud over a woven wall.

(v) A c____ stone weighing many tonnes was placed on top of a d________ as part of the burial customs of the Neolithic people.

(vi) Newgrange in County Meath is an example of a Neolithic p________ t______.

(vii) Bronze Age people would sometimes cook meat in a rectangular hole in the ground called a f________ f______.

(viii) The three types of Bronze Age burial tombs were: W______ tombs, C______ graves and S______ stones which were sometimes known as M________.

(ix) Celtic society was divided up into different t______ and each one was ruled by a king called a ____ who was the head of the royal family or d____________.

(x) The nobles in Celtic society were known as the A___ D____.

(xi) The Hill of Tara in County Meath is a good example of a h____ fort.

(xii) A dwelling surrounded by water that could only be accessed by a bridge or boat was called a c_________.

(xiii) A Celtic method of writing is called O_______.

(xiv) The stone crosses depicting events from the Bible that were carved by monks were called H___ Crosses.

(xv) The cup used to hold the wine during Mass is called a c________.

(d) Explain each term:

(i) Microlith (ii) Megalith (iii) Monolith

(e) Match each type of feature (1-4) in Column A with the locations in Ireland in Column B.

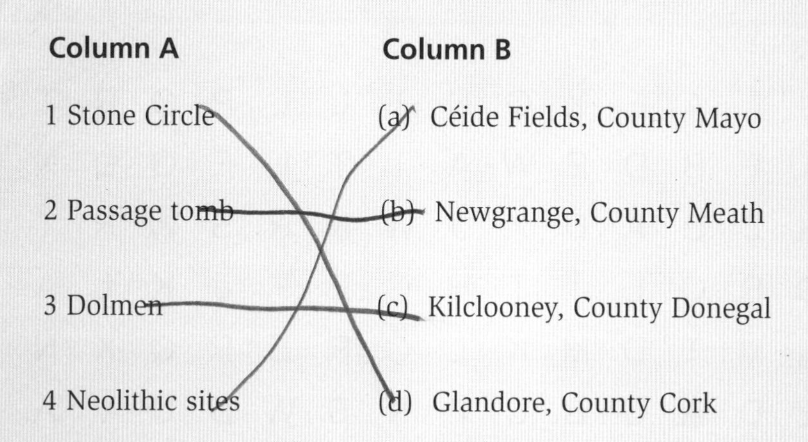


(f) Under the headings (a), (b) and (c) below, list the following:

(i) The types of food that people ate
(ii) The tools, crafts and jewellery they made
(iii) A brief description of their houses and burial tombs

(a) Mesolithic
(8000 BC – 3500 BC)
Hunter-gatherers

(b) Neolithic
(3500 BC – 2000 BC)
Farmers

(c) Bronze Age
(2000 BC – 500 BC)
Farmers

(g) In the Iron Age (500 BC – AD 400) describe the following:

(i) The types of houses and forts the people built

(ii) The way their society was organised and the clothes they wore

(iii) The religious festivals they celebrated.

(h) Find the following words in the wordsearch below:

| | | | |
|---|---|---|---|
| Lunulae | Fosses | Daub | Abbot |
| Wattle | Chalice | Monolith | Druid |
| Kerbstone | Imbolg | Tánaiste | |
| Vellum | Microlith | Quill | |

| | | | | | | | | | | | | | | | | |
|---|---|---|---|---|---|---|---|---|---|---|---|---|---|---|---|---|
| L | U | N | U | L | A | E | X | Q | U | I | L | L | P | O | R | T |
| M | U | I | K | F | B | D | E | W | A | T | T | L | E | Q | D | X |
| X | F | G | H | J | B | A | D | X | J | W | K | R | S | W | R | T |
| P | M | I | C | R | O | L | I | T | H | G | E | F | J | K | L | A |
| C | H | B | N | M | T | D | M | K | L | C | R | E | R | Q | K | N |
| M | D | Z | E | D | A | U | B | U | F | K | B | W | D | U | V | A |
| L | G | J | F | R | D | F | O | S | S | E | S | L | B | I | C | I |
| F | H | S | F | U | V | E | L | L | U | M | T | F | C | L | D | S |
| A | L | J | Z | I | S | U | G | M | O | N | O | L | I | T | H | T |
| S | D | K | F | D | I | O | J | P | G | D | N | C | X | D | K | E |
| D | H | F | L | F | C | H | A | L | I | C | E | P | O | L | R | F |

## Question 4: PEOPLE IN HISTORY

**Using the following guidelines or hints, imagine you are a monk in Early Christian Ireland. Write about your life in a monastery:**

HINTS:

* Reasons for joining the monastery
* The work you did in the monastery
* The activities of the other monks
* The life of a monk

### Reasons for joining the monastery

⇨ You were originally a Celt who believed in the Celtic gods like Dagda, the river god Boann and Lug.

⇨ There were great festivals throughout the year like Samhain when the Celts honoured all the spirits of the Underworld or Lughnasa when they prayed for a bountiful harvest.

⇨ As you grew up, you began to hear more about a new religion called Christianity. People had come into contact with it when they were trading with Britain and there were also some missionaries who came to Ireland to spread the religion.

⇨ You met some (St. Patrick, St. Secundius and St. Auxilius) missionaries and they persuaded you to convert. You decided to join the local monastery in Clonmacnoise/Clonfert/ Kildare.

### The work you did in the monastery

⇨ You were very good at drawing and so you were asked by the head of the monastery, who is called the Abbot, to work in the scriptorium on manuscripts. These manuscripts were beautifully written, illustrated and coloured copies of the Bible.

⇨ The pages were either written on vellum (calf skin) or parchment (sheepskin). The writing was done using a quill from a goose feather and the ink was from ground-up coloured stones or plants.

⇨ There are many of these beautiful books written in different monasteries, e.g. the Book of Kells or the Book of Durrow. The oldest book is called the Cathach which means the Battle Book.

### The activities of the other monks

- All the other monks had jobs to do as well. Some monks had to do all the farming to make sure the monastery had enough food. Other monks cooked the food and the meals were served in the refectory.
- Other monks worked all day making metal objects such as chalices, crosses or boxes known as reliquaries to hold important remains of saints called relics. The metalwork is very detailed and they used really fine strips of gold and silver called filigree and precious stones.
- Some monks also worked on stone masonry. They carved beautiful images of different stories from the Bible onto High Crosses so that the local population, who could not read, understood the stories.

### The life of a monk

- Most of the day was spent either working at the different jobs that the Abbot gave his monks or praying and studying the Bible.
- Monks lived on the food prepared in the monastery. It was usually very simple food, e.g. milk, cheese, fish and vegetables.
- All the monks lived in small huts called beehive huts made from wattle and daub or from stone.
- There was a round tower in the middle of the monastery. It was used either as a bell tower or for protection if anyone tried to attack the monastery.

## Question 5:

(a) Write a paragraph about <u>two</u> of the following topics:
  (i) Forts of the Iron Age in Ireland.
  (ii) The religion of the Celts.
  (iii) Political society of the Celts in Ireland.

(b) Name <u>two</u> locations in Ireland that have provided us with archaeological evidence on the burial customs of Stone Age settlers.

(c) What evidence have archaeologists found at these sites to make them believe that people from the Stone Age believed in the afterlife?

(d) Name <u>two</u> methods of dating evidence that would have helped archaeologists estimate when the tombs were built.

## Question 1: PICTURES

### (a) Picture A

(i) Name the purple item of clothing that both men are wearing over their shoulders.

(ii) What was the name for the item of clothing worn under the purple item of clothing?

(iii) Name an item of clothing worn by women in Rome.

(iv) Name two types of food eaten by Romans.

(v) What do you think the Romans are drinking in this picture?

### (b) Picture B

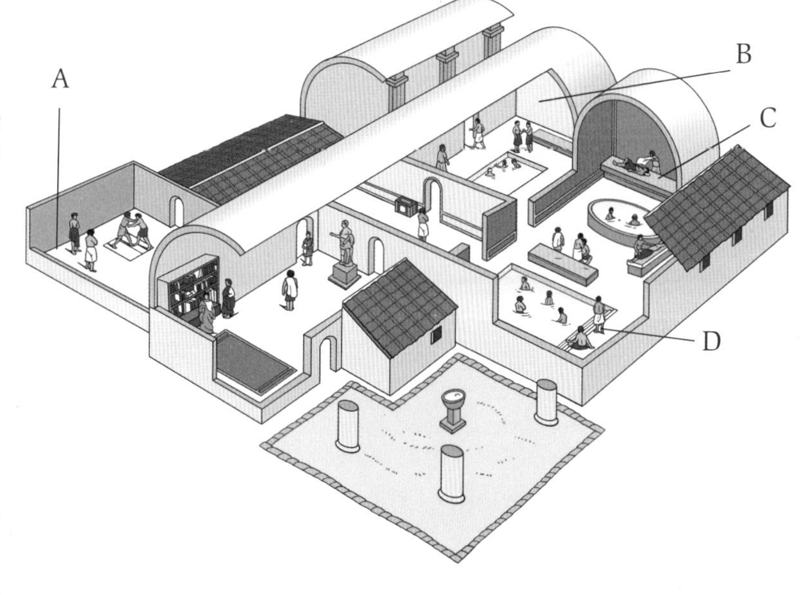


(i) Give the correct terms for the rooms marked A, B, C and D using the following clues:

**A** Where the wrestling and exercise took place

**B** A room that was hot

**C** A room for relaxation that was warm

**D** A room that was cold

(ii) What was the name given to the small curved rod that was used for scraping dirt from the men's bodies?

(iii) List two other locations where Romans spent their leisure time.

(iv) Name the sports or activities that were associated with the two locations chosen.

## (c) Picture C

(i) Name two weapons and three items of armour that the Roman soldier has in Picture C.

(ii) What is the name given to soldiers like this one who fought on foot?

(iii) Give the name of the soldiers who fought on horseback.

(iv) Write a paragraph about the life of a Roman soldier. (Note: Mention at least 10 points.)

## Question 2: DOCUMENTS

Study Documents **1a** and **b** and **2a** and **b** below, and then answer the questions that follow.

**(a)**

### Document 1a

The following is an extract from *The Golden Ass* by Apuleius written around AD 165.

Their skins were seamed all over with the marks of old floggings, as you could see through the holes in their ragged shirts that shaded rather than covered their scarred backs; but some wore only loin-cloths. They had letters marked on their foreheads, and half-shaved heads and irons on their legs.

### Document 1b

The following is an extract from *Agriculture* by Columella written around AD 50.

Women slaves ought to be rewarded for the bearing of a certain number of children. I have granted exemption from work and sometimes even freedom after they have reared many children.

(i) Why would the slaves' skins be 'seamed all over'?

(ii) Describe the clothes the slaves were wearing.

(iii) Give two methods mentioned in the first extract that slave owners used to prevent the slaves from escaping.

(iv) Why did the second author believe that female slaves ought to be rewarded?

(v) From your reading of these extracts, do you think that slaves were treated well by their masters? Give reasons, using evidence from the text.

(vi) From your studies, list three types of jobs that slaves might be expected to perform.

(vii) Where did Roman soldiers take slaves from?

(viii) How do you think slaves felt about their masters? Give reasons for your answer.

## (b) Document 2

### 2a

This is an extract from *Moral Epistles* written in AD 60 by Seneca describing the fate of the gladiators.

*The gladiators have nothing to protect them: their bodies are utterly open to every blow: every thrust finds its mark . . . Most people prefer this kind of thing to all other matches . . . The sword is not checked by helmet or shield. What good is armour? What good is swordsmanship? All these things only put off death a little. In the morning, men are matched with lions and bears, at noon with their spectators . . . death is the fighter's only exit.*

### 2b

This is an extract by Sventonius on Julius Caesar, written c. AD 110.

*His public shows were of great variety . . . Wild-beast hunts took place five days running, and the entertainment ended with a battle between two armies, each consisting of 500 infantry, twenty elephants, and thirty cavalry . . . Such huge numbers of visitors flocked to these shows from all directions that many of them had to sleep in tents pitched along the streets or roads, or on rooftops; and often the pressure of the crowd crushed people to death.*

(i) In Seneca's description of the gladiatorial battles in 2a, do the gladiators have any armour? Give reasons for your answer using evidence from the text.

(ii) What does he mean by 'death is the fighter's only exit'?

(iii) Apart from gladiators, what kind of entertainment was offered, according to the author of 2b?

(iv) Describe the battle that ended the entertainment.

(v) In 2b, how can you tell if the public enjoyed the games? Give evidence from the text to support your answer.

(vi) Do you think that Seneca (2a) enjoyed the games? Give evidence from the text to support your answer.

(vii) Do you think gladiator fighting was an enjoyable entertainment? Give reasons for your answer.

## Question 3: SHORT-ANSWER QUESTIONS

(a) Explain the following terms:

| | | | | | |
|---|---|---|---|---|---|
| (i) | Senator | (viii) | Manumission | (xv) | Gladiator |
| (ii) | Republic | (ix) | Atrium | (xvi) | Aqueduct |
| (iii) | Patrician | (x) | Tunic | (xvii) | Tepidarium |
| (iv) | Plebeian | (xi) | Toga | (xviii) | *Decimatio* |
| (v) | Domus | (xii) | Stola | (xix) | Polytheism |
| (vi) | Insulae | (xiii) | Thermopolia | (xx) | Oration |
| (vii) | Cena | (xiv) | Colosseum | (xxi) | Rhetoric |

(b) What sports took place at the following locations:
(i) Colosseum (ii) Circus Maximus

(c) Give the name for each of the gladiators in the pictures:

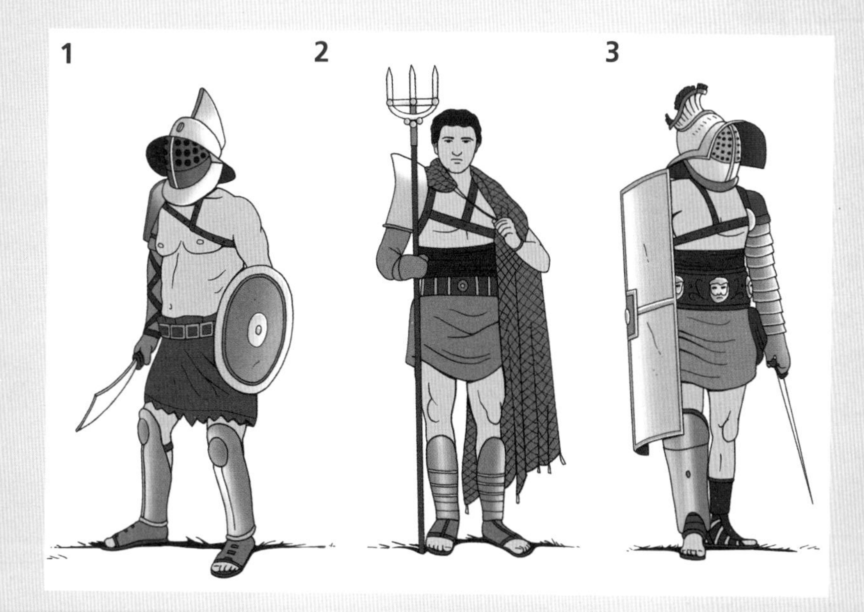


(d) Give the Roman name for each of these parts of a Roman domus and buildings:

(i) Central open square
(ii) A small pool in the middle of the central square
(iii) Walled garden with shrines to family gods
(iv) The kitchen
(v) The bedrooms
(vi) Large apartment blocks for plebeians
(vii) Takeaways for plebeians

(e) Match the gods in Column A to their relevant area of responsibility in Column B:

| Column A | Column B |
|---|---|
| 1 Neptune | (a) War |
| 2 Jupiter | (b) Civilisation, wisdom and war |
| 3 Minerva | (c) The Ocean and the sea |
| 4 Mars | (d) The Underworld and wealth |
| 5 Pluto | (e) King of gods, thunder and lightning |

(f) (i) Write the following numbers in Roman numerals: (a) 65 (b) 7 (c) 1999
(ii) Write the Roman numerals in numbers: (a) MMX (b) MCMLIX

(g) Fill in the gaps: Rewrite the following sentences and fill in the missing words:
(i) Legend states that Rome was founded by R_________ and R________.
(ii) A___________ Caesar was the first Emperor of Rome.
(iii) Mount V____________ erupted in AD 79 and destroyed the city of P_________ and H__________________.
(iv) In the Roman army, a l______ was made up of ten c_____ and that was made up of six c_______. Each soldier was called a l_______________.
(v) Roman soldiers ate a soup made from barley called g_______.
(vi) Wealthy citizens of Rome were called p___________ while poorer Romans were called p________.
(vii) P___________ lived in large houses called a d_______.
(viii) Roman men wore t______ over their t________, while women wore s________.
(ix) The main meal of the day was called the ________.
(x) Chariot racing took place at the C______ M________, while gladiator fights took place at the C___________.
(xi) Roman a_______ would predict the future by looking at the entrails of a dead animal.
(xii) The Underworld was ruled by P______ and the entrance was guarded by a three-headed dog called C_______.
(xiii) The Christians were persecuted by the Romans until Emperor C___________ officially converted to Christianity.
(xiv) It is thought that the Romans were the first in Europe to discover c______ by mixing lime, water and ash.
(xv) A___________s were large structures that brought water into the city for the population.
(xvi) The language of Rome was called L______.

## Question 4: PEOPLE IN HISTORY

**Using the following facts or hints, write an account of a young person in any ancient civilisation outside Ireland. Remember to state which civilisation you are describing, in this case, Rome. Write the account pretending you are the person. In this account, the young person is a boy, so if you are a girl, you could make the person your brother.**

HINTS:

* Education
* Clothing
* Religion
* Food and meals
* Pastimes

### Education

⇨ I was born into a wealthy Patrician family in Rome and I live in a domus (mention the peristylium, atrium, impluvium, culina and cubicula).

⇨ I have friends who are not so wealthy and they are known as plebeians and live in insulae.

⇨ I have been attending school since I was seven and I am learning reading, writing and arithmetic. When I turn 12 I will be sent to a new school for only boys. Here we will learn Greek and Roman history and literature. We will also learn about grammar, geometry and arithmetic.

⇨ We will also read the works of great Greek and Roman writers such as Homer, Ovid and Virgil.

⇨ To help me become a successful politician, I need to practise my rhetoric and oration, i.e. how to argue and speak in public.

⇨ If I break my abacus or stylus and tablet, I am flogged.

⇨ My sister stays at home and is learning how to spin, weave, embroider and arrange flowers. She will need all these skills when she gets married in a few years and becomes a matriarch in her own house.

### Food and meals

⇨ Every day I have dinner which is called the cena. Sometimes my parents have musicians at the cena.

⇨ We eat all sorts of food such as dormice, olives, dates and also lots of meat such as pig, boar and lobster.

⇨ My friends sometimes go to the thermopolia to get takeaway food as they do not have a kitchen in their insulae.

### Clothing

⇨ I wear a tunic all day. My father wears a toga over his tunic and my mother wears a stola with a palla over it to keep her warm.

## Pastimes

- Sometimes I go to the Colosseum to see the gladiators fight. There are three types of gladiator: the Thracian, the Samnite and the Retiarius.
- We also go to the Circus Maximus to watch one of the chariot races. My favourite team is the greens!
- I also like going to the theatre to see the funny plays of Plautus and Terence. At the theatre the actors all wear funny masks.

## Religion

- We often have to go to the temples to make sacrifices to the gods. My father wanted to find out what will happen in the future so he went to the augur who looked into the entrails of a bird.
- My father's friend died recently so we will have to go to the funeral. He paid for professional mourners to come along and cry at the funeral. The person is going to be buried along the Via Appia.
- Hopefully he won't go to Tartarus, which is where all the bad people go for punishment in the Underworld.
- We will put a coin on his eyes so that he can pay the ferryman Charon to get him across the River Styx.

## Question 5:

(a) Write a paragraph about three of the following:

(i) Pompeii

(ii) Roman religion

(iii) Roman homes

(iv) Roman funerals

(b) Give three ways in which we can learn about Roman life and customs.

(c) Explain the connection between the night sky and Rome.

(d) (i) Outline three ways in which Roman civilisation has influenced the world around us today.

(ii) Do you think the influences on our lives have been positive or negative? Give reasons for your answer.

# Chapter 4
# The Middle Ages

## Question 1: PICTURES

### (a) Picture A

**Look at A1 and A2 above.**

(i) State which architectural style each one is.

(ii) Using A1 and A2, give two examples of Gothic and Romanesque architecture.

(iii) Give one other difference between the two styles that you have not mentioned in your answer to question (ii) above.

(iv) Explain the word 'cathedral'.

(v) Look at A3 and A4 and name the architectural features at X and Y.

## (b) Picture B

**Look at Picture B above of a castle from the Middle Ages and answer the questions below.**

(i) Give the correct name for each of the parts of the castle marked A-F.

(ii) Give the main advantage of stone castles as opposed to wooden motte and bailey castles.

(iii) From picture B above, give <u>two</u> ways in which soldiers were able to defend the castle.

(iv) Give <u>three</u> methods by which soldiers would attack or besiege a castle during the Middle Ages.

Study Documents **1** and **2** below, and then answer the questions that follow.

## (a) Document 1

This is an extract from the Prologue in Chaucer's *The Canterbury Tales*.

With curly locks, as if they had been pressed.
He was some twenty years of age, I guessed.
In stature he was of a moderate length,
With wonderful agility and strength.
He'd seen some service with the cavalry
In Flanders and Artois and Picardy . . .
Short was his gown, the sleeves were long and wide;
He knew the way to sit a horse and ride.
He could make songs and poems and recite,
Knew how to joust and dance, to draw and write.

(i) Describe the appearance of the knight.

(ii) What does the term 'seen some service with the cavalry' mean?

(iii) At which places had the knight fought?

(iv) Apart from fighting, what does the author state that the knight 'knew how to' do?

(v) Describe what a 'joust' was.

(vi) Outline the stages a boy had to go through to became a knight.

(vii) Describe in detail the ceremony that occurred when a boy finally became a knight.

## (b) Document 2

The following is an extract from a report on the spread of the Black Death by Giovanni Boccaccio in his book *The Decameron* written in approximately 1530.

*What I am about to say is incredible to hear, and if I and others had not witnessed it with our own eyes, I should not dare believe it (let alone write about it), no matter how trustworthy a person I might have heard it from. This pestilence (disease) was so powerful that it was communicated to the healthy by contact with the sick, the way a fire close to dry or oily things will set them aflame. And the evil of the plague went even further: not only did talking to or being around the sick bring infection and a common death, but also touching the clothes of the sick or anything touched or used by them seemed to communicate this very disease in the person involved.*

(i) What does Boccaccio state to show the reader that he was not exaggerating?

(ii) According to the author, how is the disease similar to a fire?

(iii) List three ways the author states that a person can contract (get) the disease.

(iv) From your studies, what was the cause of the Black Death?

(v) Is this a primary or secondary source? Give reasons for your answer.

## Question 3: SHORT-ANSWER QUESTIONS

(a) Explain the following terms:

| | | | | | |
|---|---|---|---|---|---|
| (i) | Demesne | (vii) | Pannage | (xiii) | Curfew |
| (ii) | Motte and bailey | (viii) | Fallow | (xiv) | Bailiff |
| (iii) | Joust | (ix) | Dubbing | (xv) | Flail |
| (iv) | Guild | (x) | Page | (xvi) | Sickle |
| (v) | Journeyman | (xi) | Squire | (xvii) | Charter |
| (vi) | Tithe | (xii) | Lance | (xviii) | Toll |

(b) Write a paragraph explaining how the feudal system worked.

(c) Explain what occurred in the following rooms of a medieval castle:

(i) the Solar
(ii) the Great Hall
(iii) the Dungeon
(iv) the Chapel
(v) the Latrine

(d) List <u>four</u> things that might be served at a feast in a medieval castle.

(e) Why were spices so important to the cooking of food in medieval times?

(f) Look at the picture of a knight. Name the weapons and armour that are marked A, B, C, D, E and F.

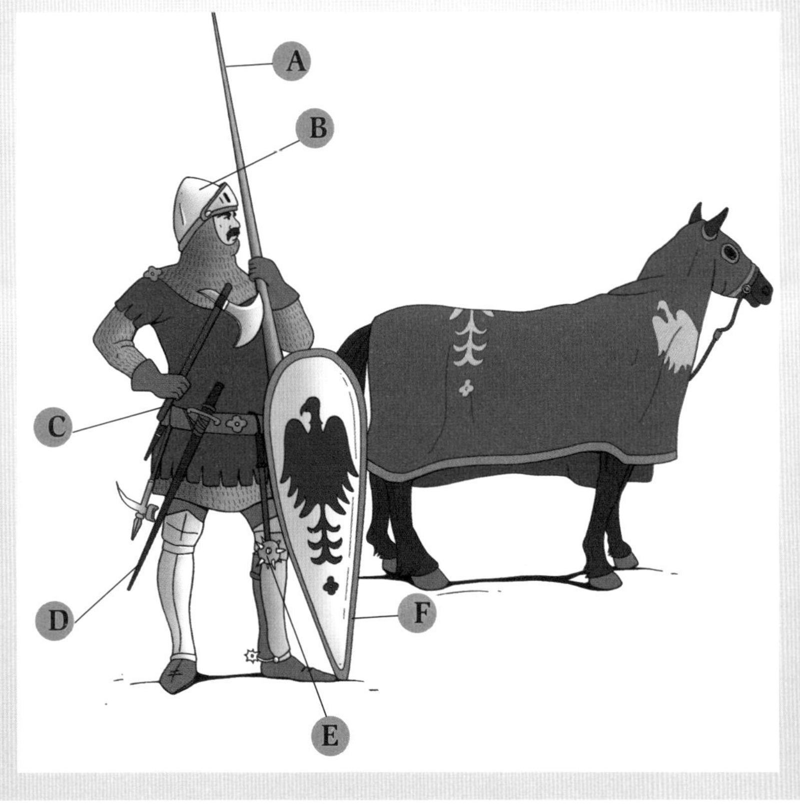

(g) Fill in the gaps: Rewrite the following sentences and fill in the missing words.

(i) Under the f________ s________, kings would give land to their v________ and in return, the v______ would swear an oath of h_________ to the king.

(ii) These v______ were known as the n_______ or aristocracy.

(iii) The n_________ lived in small castles or large houses called m_______ h_______. Around the m_______ there was a village where the local people lived.

(iv) There were two types of peasants: f________ and s____.

(v) All peasants had to pay one tenth of all their earnings which was called the t______ to the church.

(vi) Peasants lived in small one- or two-roomed houses made from w_____ and d_____.

(vii) The main food that peasants ate was a thick vegetable soup mixed with wheat or barley and beans called p_______.

(viii) The harvest was cut using a large tool called a sc_____ or a smaller hand-held one called a s______. A f_______ was used to separate the grain from the stalks.

(ix) Each town was granted a r______ ch______ from the king that permitted it to run its own affairs.

(x) Each town had a m______ s______ at its centre where people could sell their produce.

(xi) A f_____ took place once a year on land outside the town where exotic goods from all over the world were sold.

(xii) Each trade established their own g______ to set the prices and maintain certain standards.

(xiii) A c_______ forced everyone in a town to put out their fires by dark to stop a fire breaking out.

(xiv) Towns were very dirty and there were lots of diseases. The B____ D______ or B______ plague killed about one third of Europe's population.

(xv) To become a master craftsman, a person became an a_______ and then a j_______.

(xvi) The two types of medieval churches were R_____ and G______.

(xvii) F_______ b________ were used to support the walls of a G____ church.

(xviii) Richard de Clare was also known as S__________ and he married A_____, Dermot Mac M_______'s daughter.

(xix) In 1172, H_______ II, the N______ king of England was declared L____ of Ireland.

(h) Place the following names in the correct group – Gaelic or Norman.

(i) McCarthy
(vi) Devereux
(ii) FitzGerald
(v) Butler
(iii) Burke
(vii) MacMurrough

**(a) A Nobleman (Lord or Earl) in the Middle Ages. Using the following points or hints, write an account of life as a noble during medieval times. You can either write the account pretending to be that person or describing the person.**

HINTS:

* The Castle
* The Feudal System
* Food and Clothes
* Entertainment

### The Castle

- ⇨ Medieval nobility lived in stone castles. There were large curtain walls with turrets and portcullises for protection.
- ⇨ The walls surrounded the bailey where the soldiers and servants worked.
- ⇨ The noble lived in the keep which was a large stone building in the bailey.
- ⇨ The keep was cold and damp. The windows were small and thin for protection and because there was no glass, there were drafts.
- ⇨ To help heat the castle, large tapestries were put on the walls and huge fires were lit in each room.
- ⇨ The noble spent most of the day doing business and then eating in the Great Hall.
- ⇨ The lady of the house sometimes spent time weaving or listening to music in the solar, which was located beside the noble's apartments on the floor above the Great Hall.
- ⇨ The lord and lady attended mass in the chapel.
- ⇨ The dungeons in the cellar were used to keep food and any prisoners.

### The Feudal System

- ⇨ The king gave land to a nobleman in return for the noble's oath of homage or loyalty.
- ⇨ The noble also promised to pay some rent to the king and provide knights and soldiers for the king if the king went to war or was in danger.
- ⇨ The noble/lord then rented out his land to other small farmers or to peasants who paid him rent. A few times throughout the year, the peasants and serfs worked on the lord's land.
- ⇨ This system was called the feudal system.

### Food and Clothes

- At the big feasts, the lord ate large amounts of meat: boar, rabbit, pork, beef, venison, goose, pheasant and hare were all eaten.
- Very few vegetables were eaten, but the meat was cooked in rich sauces with lots of spices.
- There were no fridges to keep the meat so it was often rotten. To hide the smell, the chefs used lots of spices.
- The food was served on a piece of stale bread called a trencher and knives, spoons and fingers were used to eat.
- Wine, beer or mead was drunk while musicians or jesters entertained the diners.
- Clothes were woven mostly by the women of the castle. The clothes were heavy to keep people warm. Silk was sometimes used for special clothes that were brightly coloured using dyes from ground plants, stones and fruits.

### Entertainment

- The noble often went hunting wild deer, boar and foxes.
- Hawking (using a trained hawk to catch small animals) was also popular.
- Lords attended tournaments for knights to see them joust or compete for prizes in mock battles.

**(b) A Peasant Farmer in the Middle Ages. Using the following points or hints, write an account of life as a peasant farmer during medieval times. You can either write the account pretending to be that person or describing the person.**

HINTS:

* Housing
* Food and Clothing
* Work throughout the year
* Pastimes

### Housing

- Peasants lived in small one- or two-roomed cottages. These houses were made from wattle and daub and had dried straw called thatch on the roof.
- There were no windows and so the smoke from the fire had to go out through a small hole in the roof. This made the room smoky and dark.
- The whole family lived in this room. They cooked, ate and slept in the room and during bad weather they brought the animals inside too.

### Food and Clothing

- Clothes were made using the wool from the sheep. A rough linen was sometimes made from flax. The clothes were coloured using dye from berries and plants.
- Shoes were made from animal hides.
- Food was very simple: vegetable soup called pottage, eggs, onions and cabbages were all used as well as barley and wheat. Nuts and berries were collected from the forest.
- Milk from a cow was drunk and made into cheese and butter.
- Meat was only eaten on very special occasions such as Easter or Christmas.

### Work throughout the year

- There was work to do every day throughout the year. The lord's land had to be ploughed, sown, weeded and then harvested and threshed. The grain was then ground into flour.
- During the autumn, wild berries, mushrooms and nuts were collected from the forest.
- Some animals were killed and their meat was cured to keep it for the winter.
- The fields were left fallow every third year so that it could regain some of its nutrients.

### Pastimes

- On Sunday peasants had the day off as it was a holy day.
- Peasants spent their leisure time playing board games like chess or draughts or betting on cock-fighting and badger-baiting.

## Question 5:

**(a) Write a paragraph on two of the following:**

(i) Norman influence in Ireland.

(ii) The Norman invasion of Ireland.

(iii) Crime and punishment in medieval towns.

(b) Describe briefly where medieval towns developed.

(c) Write an account of the training required to become a master craftsman.

(d) (i) What were guilds in medieval towns?

(ii) Describe how a guild operated.

# Chapter 5

# The Renaissance

## Question 1: PICTURES

### (a) Picture A

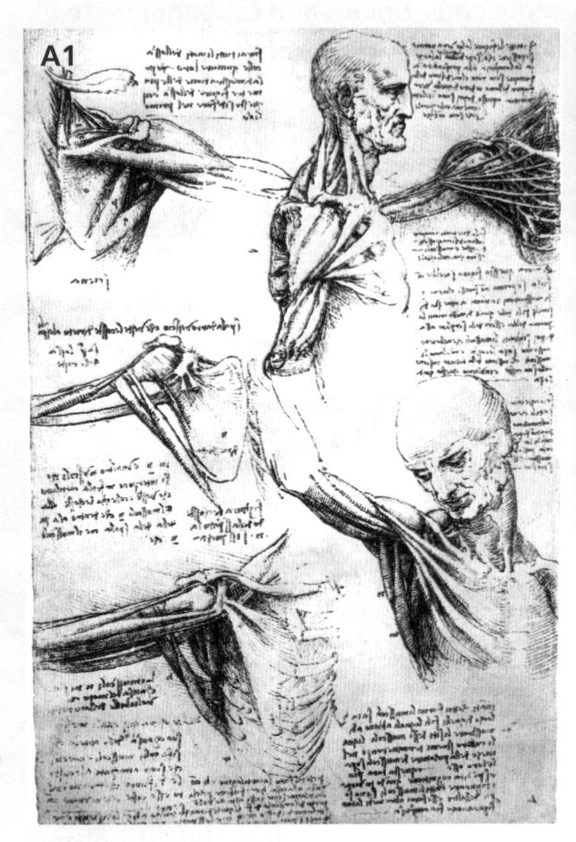


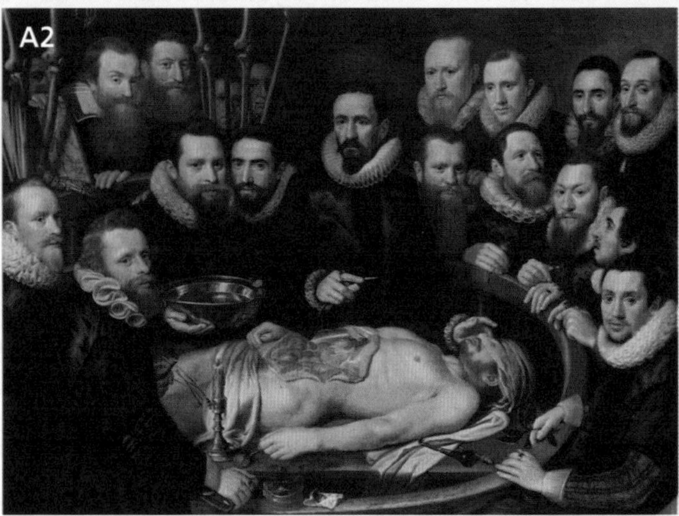


**The sketches (A1) are by Leonardo da Vinci and the painting (A2) is by Pieter van Miereveldd.**

(i) What is the term given to the study of the working of the human body?

(ii) Why were Renaissance artists interested in sketching the muscles and bodies of humans?

(iii) Name a Renaissance physician and the discovery for which they are famous.

## (b) Picture B

B1

B2

**Look at B1 and B2 and answer the following questions:**

(i) Using evidence from these paintings, state how you know that they were from the Renaissance. Give one reason for each painting – making reference to that painting.

(ii) State two other differences between paintings from the Middle Ages and those of the Renaissance. Do not include any differences mentioned in your answer to (i) above.

(iii) Name a Renaissance painter from Italy and one of their works.

(iv) Name a Renaissance painter from outside Italy and one of their works.

## (c) Picture C

**Picture C above is of a printing press at work. Examine the picture and answer the following questions:**

(i) State what is occurring at each of the places marked A, B, C and D.

(ii) Give a brief outline on how the moveable-type printing press worked.

(iii) Who is thought to have invented the moveable-type printing press?

(iv) Give <u>one</u> advantage that a printed book had over a handwritten manuscript.

(v) Explain why some people believe that the printing press was the most important invention of the Renaissance.

Study Documents **1** and **2** below, and then answer the questions that follow.

## (a) Document 1

This is an extract from an article on the city of Florence during the Renaissance from *National Geographic*, June 1967 – written by Joseph Judge.

*Firenze Bella. Beautiful Florence, the mother country of Western man. It is fair to say that much of what we know today of painting and sculpture, of architecture and political science, of scientific method and economic theory, we owe to the artists, politicians, statesmen, bankers, and merchants of the Renaissance — that explosion of intellectual and artistic energy in Italy between 1300 and 1600. And Florentines stood at the turbulent center of the Renaissance . . .*

*In Florence, Galileo pursued his studies of motion that would lead eventually to Newton and the law of gravity. First man to gaze through a telescope upon the moons of Jupiter and the lunar landscape, Galileo changed forever our concept of the universe.*

*Here Machiavelli, watching in his own time the tragic progress from autocracy to republicanism to tyranny, left a legacy of political thought that still instructs statesmen.*

*But Florence's greatest glory was its galaxy of artists—Cimabue and his great pupil Giotto; Masaccio, Uccello, Fra Filippo Lippi, Botticelli, Leonardo da Vinci; the sculptors Ghiberti, Donatello, and mighty Michelangelo; the architects Brunelleschi, Alberti, Michelozzo, to name but a few. Many of their works remain in place in a city essentially unchanged for 400 years.*

(i) List three areas of knowledge that the author believes we owe to the artists, politicians, statesmen, bankers and merchants of the Renaissance.

(ii) What was Galileo the first man to do?

(iii) What was Florence's greatest glory?

(iv) List three of the artists referred to in this document and name a work by each artist.

(v) Why does the author describe 'Beautiful Florence' as being 'the mother country of Western man'?

(vi) From your knowledge of the Renaissance, do you agree with the author? Give reasons for your answer.

## (b) Document 2

*This is an extract from Leonardo da Vinci's letter to Duke Ludovico Sforza of Milan.*

> I have plans for bridges very light and strong and suitable for carrying very easily . . .. I have plans for destroying every fortress or other stronghold unless it has been founded upon rock . . . I have also plans for making cannon, very convenient and easy of transport, with which to hurl small stones in the manner almost of hail . . .. I will make covered chariots, safe and unassailable, which, entering among the enemy with their artillery there is no body of men so great but they would break them . . . I can make cannon mortars and light ordnance of very beautiful shapes, quite different from those in ordinary use.

(i) List five of the inventions that Leonardo claimed to be able to make.

(ii) Why do you think he might want to stress his ability at making weapons of warfare rather than his skills at painting?

(iii) What benefits does he claim his cannon has?

(iv) Why did Leonardo later leave Milan?

(v) List two pieces of art that Leonardo created.

## Question 3: SHORT-ANSWER QUESTIONS

(a) Match the following Renaissance artists in Column A with the correct work of art in Column B:

| Column A | Column B |
|---|---|
| 1 Leonardo da Vinci | (a) Statue of *David* |
| | (b) *School of Athens* |
| 2 Raphael | (c) *Mona Lisa* |
| | (d) *The Last Supper* |
| 3 Rembrandt | (e) The Sistine Chapel |
| | (f) *The Night Watch* |
| 4 Michelangelo | (g) *The Pièta* |
| | (h) *Marriage of the Virgin* |

(b) Write a sentence explaining how the following people were connected with the Renaissance:

(i) Cosimo de Medici
(ii) Giorgio Vasari
(iii) Leonardo da Vinci
(iv) Albrecht Dürer
(v) Rembrandt Harmenszoon van Rijn
(vi) Johannes Gutenberg
(vii) William Caxton
(viii) William Shakespeare
(ix) Niccolò Machiavelli
(x) Andreas Vesalius
(xi) William Harvey
(xii) Galen
(xiii) Nicolaus Copernicus
(xiv) Galileo Galilei
(xv) Jan Lippershey

(c) Fill in the gaps: Rewrite the following sentences and fill in the missing words:

(i) The word Renaissance comes from the French word for r_ -b_______.

(ii) Many people became interested in the art, architecture, philosophy and science of ancient G______ and R______.

(iii) The Renaissance began in I______ which was made up of many different c___-s____ such as Milan, V______, F_______, Genoa and Naples.

(iv) Wealthy bankers and merchants known as p_______ paid artists to create beautiful pieces of art.

(v) One of the richest families were bankers from F______ called de M_______.

(vi) Cosimo de M_______ was a great p______ of the arts. His grandson L________ was known as L________ the Magnificent because of his generosity towards artists due to his great love of the arts.

(vii) Artists studied a________ to help them understand the workings of the body so that their paintings would look more realistic.

(viii) A v__________ point was used to create p____________. This gave a painting more depth.

(ix) When a painting is painted directly onto wet plaster on walls it is called a f_______.

(x) Michelangelo painted the ceiling and wall of the S_________ C________ in Rome.

(xi) Johannes G________ was thought to have invented the m______-t______ printing press.

(xii) William S_____________ was born in Stratford-on-Avon. He wrote 38 p_____, 154 s_______ and a number of poems. His p_____ were performed in the G_____ Theatre.

(xiii) Andreas V_________ drew 270 pictures of human muscles, bones, heart and brains in his book called *On the S_________ of the Human Body*.

(xiv) Nicolaus C__________ outlined his views that the earth and other planets moved around the sun in his book *On the Revolution of H________ Bodies*.

(d) Name the following people (1-5) and state what they were famous for.

(e) Explain the following words:

(i) Renaissance
(ii) Anatomy
(iii) Philosophy
(iv) Patron
(v) Vanishing point
(vi) Fresco
(vii) Botany
(viii) *Sfumato*
(ix) Vernacular
(x) Humanism
(xi) Engravings
(xii) *Pièta*
(xiii) Perspective

(f) Match the following men in Column A with what they are famous for in Column B:

| **Column A** | **Column B** |
|---|---|
| 1 Johannes Gutenberg | (a) Proving the circular flow of blood around the body |
| 2 Niccolò Machiavelli | (b) Author of *On the Structure of the Human Body* |
| 3 William Shakespeare | (c) The moveable-type printing press |
| 4 Andreas Vesalius | (d) The belief that the earth orbited the sun |
| 5 William Harvey | (e) Author of *The Prince* |
| 6 Galileo Galilei | (f) The Globe Theatre in London |

## Question 4: PEOPLE IN HISTORY

**(a) Using the following facts or hints, write an account of a named artist in Italy during the Renaissance.**

HINTS:

* Name and early life
* His other interest
* Later life
* His paintings

### Name and early life

- Leonardo was born in the town of Vinci near Florence in 1452.
- He showed ability in drawing and painting and was sent to be an apprentice to Andrea Verrocchio in Florence aged 14.
- He painted the angel on the left of Verrocchio's *The Baptism of Christ* which was so good that Verrocchio decided to quit painting as he felt he couldn't compete.
- He lived in Florence working on many different projects before moving to Milan in 1482 to work for the Duke of Milan, Ludovico Sforza.
- He moved back to Florence in 1499 when the French army invaded Milan.

### His paintings

- While in Milan he painted *The Virgin on the Rocks* (1485) and a fresco called *The Last Supper* (1497) on the wall of the Santa Maria delle Grazie monastery.
- After moving back to Florence he painted a portrait of the wife of a wealthy merchant called the *Mona Lisa* (1506).
- In *The Last Supper* it is possible to see the use of perspective. Leonardo also attempted to use a new method of painting frescoes but it was not successful and *The Last Supper* has suffered from flaking ever since.
- Leonardo also used a painting technique called *sfumato* which means smoky. This method made the skin of the person seem soft.

### His other interests

- He was constantly writing his ideas into his notebooks. There are still over 5,000 pages of his notes. He was left-handed and wrote backwards to stop people stealing his ideas.
- His notebooks show sketches of many different inventions such as catapults, tanks, parachutes, cannons and helicopters.
- He was also interested in astronomy, geology and botany.
- His interest in anatomy helped him to paint people more accurately. He dissected over 30 bodies to help him understand how the human body worked.

### Later Life

- In 1513 Leonardo moved to Rome to work for Pope Leo X and then moved to Paris in 1519 to work for King Francis I.
- He died in 1519 aged 67 believing that he never achieved his potential.

**(b) Using the facts or hints below, write an account of a named artist from outside Italy during the Renaissance.**

HINTS:

* Early life
* His paintings
* Later life

### Early life

- Rembrandt Harmenszoon van Rijn was born in Leiden, the Netherlands in 1606.
- He studied at the University of Leiden before moving to Amsterdam in 1631.
- He married Saskia van Uylengurg in 1634 and had four children with her, although only one boy survived childhood.
- Saskia died in 1642.

### His paintings

- He painted roughly 400 paintings, 1,400 drawings and etchings and about 60 self-portraits.
- His paintings were often religious scenes with many people in the picture.
- *The Anatomy Lesson of Dr. Tulp* (1632) shows Rembrandt's interest in group compositions and different facial expressions on each of the doctors. *(See also picture A2 at the beginning of the chapter)*
- He painted *Belshazzar's feast* (1635) which shows his use of dramatic light and shade.
- His most famous painting is *The Night Watch* (1642). He was commissioned by some city guardsmen to paint them as they prepared to go to work. It was originally called *The Shooting Company of Captain Frans Banning Cocq* but it got so dirty that people thought the scene was at night.
- Again, Rembrandt uses dramatic light and shade and group compositions in *The Night Watch*.

### Later life

- Rembrandt was declared bankrupt in 1656 and had to sell his house along with all of his antiques and art collection.
- His surviving son, Titus, died in 1668 and Rembrandt himself died a year later and was buried in an unmarked grave in Amsterdam.

**(c) Using the facts or hints below, write an account of a scientist or physician during the Renaissance.**

HINTS:

* Early life
* Discoveries
* Later life

### Early life

- Galileo Galilei was born near Pisa in Italy in 1564.
- He studied medicine in the University of Pisa in 1581 before changing to philosophy and mathematics.
- He was appointed as chair of mathematics at the University of Padua in 1592 when he was only 24 years old.

### Discoveries

- During his time in Pisa he was able to prove that objects fell to earth at the same speed regardless of the weight of the object. He expressed this proof in a mathematic formula.
- After hearing about the invention of the telescope by the Dutchman Jan Lippershey in 1608, Galileo created his own telescope.
- Using his telescope he was able to see that the moon had mountains and craters on its surface, the Milky Way was made up of hundreds of small stars and there were four moons circling Jupiter.
- After making these discoveries, Galileo decided that the Polish astronomer Nicolaus Copernicus was right in thinking that the earth circled the sun and not the other way around.
- He wrote a book outlining his discoveries called *Dialogue on the Two Chief World Systems* in 1632.

### Later life

- Galileo was asked to come in front of the Church's Inquisition to explain his views on how the earth orbited the sun as they were contrary to the Church's teachings.
- The trial lasted for several months and it seemed likely that Galileo would be found guilty and burnt at the stake.
- He reluctantly agreed to withdraw his views and returned to his home in Florence where he was forbidden to leave his house or to have any guests for the rest of his life.
- He became blind in 1637 and died in 1642.

**(d) Using the facts or hints given below, write an account of a writer during the Renaissance.**

HINTS:
* Early life
* His writings
* Later life

**Early life**

⇨ William Shakespeare was born in Stratford-on-Avon in 1564.

⇨ At age 18, he married Anne Hathaway and they had three children.

⇨ He moved to London and by 1592 he was acting and writing poems and plays.

⇨ His first play, *The Comedy of Errors*, was performed in 1594.

⇨ He became part owner of a theatrical company called The King's Men and they opened a theatre called The Globe on the banks of the river Thames.

**His writings**

⇨ Shakespeare wrote 38 plays which were extremely popular and made him very famous and wealthy.

⇨ His plays can be divided into three types: comedies, histories and tragedies:

Comedies, e.g. *The Comedy of Errors* and *Twelfth Night*

Histories, e.g. *Julius Caesar, Henry V* and *Antony and Cleopatra*

Tragedies, e.g. *Romeo and Juliet, Hamlet, Othello, King Lear* and *Macbeth*.

⇨ His plays are still popular as they deal with issues that are still relevant today: power, justice, love and death.

⇨ He also created realistic characters with strengths but also with flaws.

⇨ He wrote 154 rhyming poems of 14 lines in length called sonnets and a number of other poems mostly about love.

**Later life**

⇨ The Globe Theatre was destroyed by a fire caused by a cannonball in 1613.

⇨ Around the time of the fire, Shakespeare retired back to Stratford and died in 1616.

## Question 5:

(a) Give one lasting consequence of the Renaissance on European society.

(b) Write a paragraph on the importance of the following on the beginning of the Renaissance:
   (i) The Medici family
   (ii) Italian city-states in the fifteenth century.

(c) Choose any one piece of Renaissance art that you have studied and then answer the following questions:
   (i) Name the piece of art.
   (ii) Name the artist who created the piece.
   (iii) Reasons why it is so highly thought of.
   (iv) Evidence why it is a piece from the Renaissance.

(d) Outline the changes that took place during the Renaissance in the following areas:
   (i) Architecture
   (ii) Sculpture

# Age of Exploration

Chapter 6

## Question 1: PICTURES

### (a) Picture A

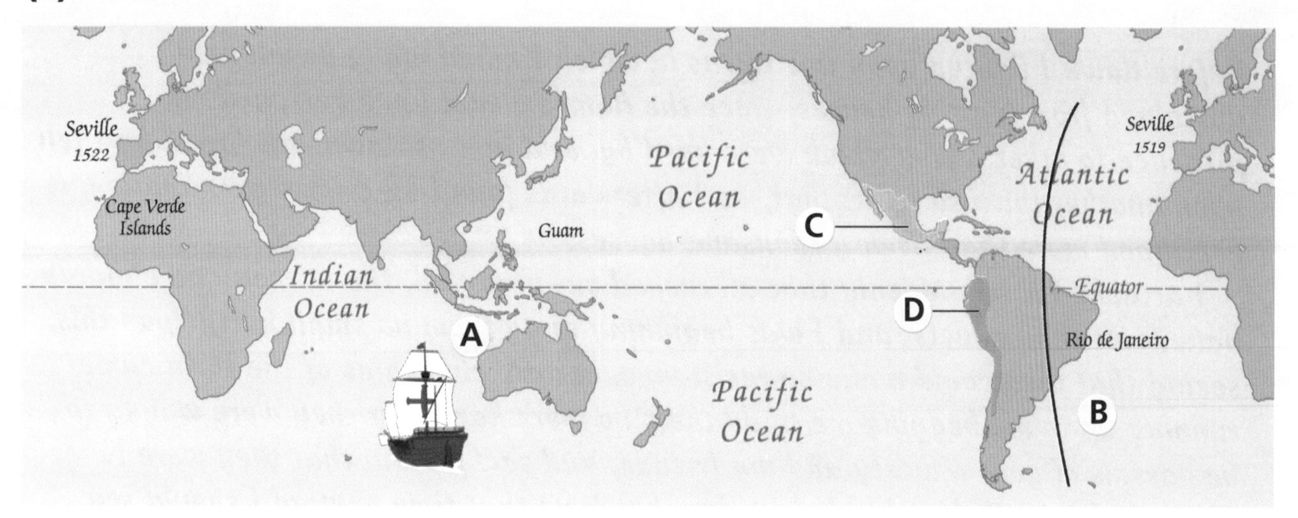


(i) Name the islands at A.

(ii) Name the treaty that created this line at B and briefly explain what the treaty established.

(iii) Name the empires at C and D.

### (b) Picture B

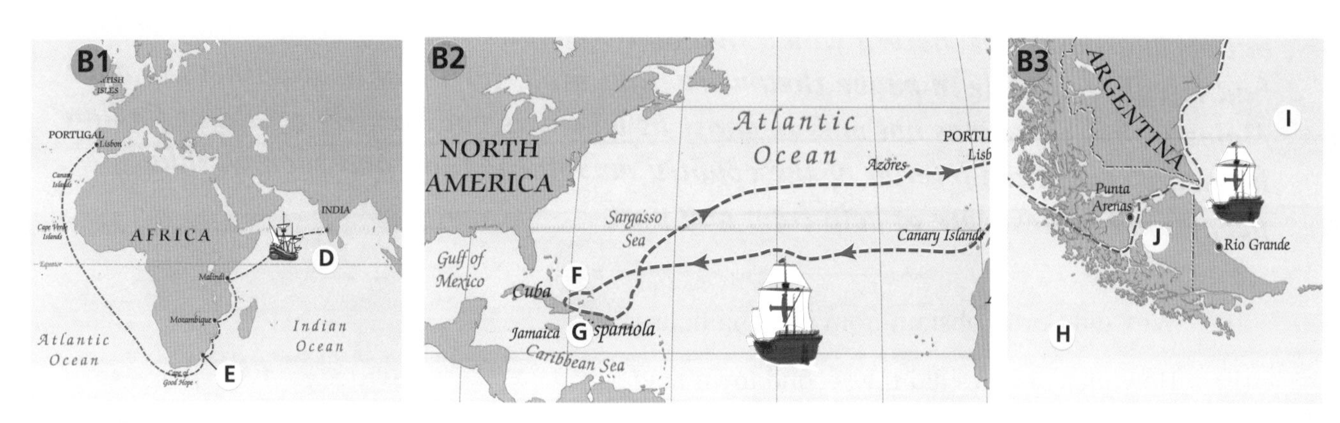


(i) Name the leaders of the voyages marked in B1 and B2.

(ii) Name the place in India marked D where the leader of the B1 voyage landed.

(iii) What is the name of the place marked E in B1 where the explorer stopped at Christmas 1497?

(iv) The explorer in B2 landed first at what island marked F?

(v) The whole group of islands marked G in B2 is called the West Indies. Explain why they are called that.

(vi) Name the oceans at H and I and the straits at J.

## Question 2: DOCUMENTS

Study Documents **1** and **2** below, and then answer the questions that follow.

### (a) Document 1

This is an extract from a letter sent by Hernando Cortés to the King of Spain.

*Before dawn I lighted upon two towns in which I killed many people, but abstained from burning houses, since the flames would have betrayed my presence to other towns which were hard by: and just as dawn was breaking I fell upon another town so great that, as I afterwards found by a later examination, it contained more than twenty thousand houses.*

*I attacked it so suddenly that all rushed out unarmed, the women and children naked, into the streets, and I was beginning to do them no small hurt. Upon this, seeing that they could make no resistance, certain chieftains of the town came running up to me begging me to do them no more harm, for they were willing to be vassals of your Majesty and my friends, and saw plainly that they were to blame in having refused to believe me; but from that time onward I should see that they would always do what I should bid them in your Majesty's name, and they would be your Majesty's very loyal subjects.*

*More than four thousand of them now came up to me desiring peace, and drew me aside to an excellent dish of food: and thus I left them pacified, and returning to the camp found all the men that I had left in it greatly terrified thinking that some peril had overtaken me, when they saw the horses return the night before: but on hearing of the victory which God had been pleased to give us and how I had left those people in peace they were right glad: for I can bear witness to your Majesty that there was not one amongst us who was not heartily afraid at finding himself so far in the interior of the country among so many and such warlike people and so destitute of help from any part.*

(i) Why did Cortés abstain from burning houses?

(ii) How many homes did the second town have?

(iii) How can we tell that the locals did not have any weapons?

(iv) In what ways did the local chieftains show that they were looking for peace?

(v) How many people came to Cortés to seek peace?

(vi) Why were his men 'greatly terrified' about him?

(vii) How does Cortés show the Emperor that he (Cortés) is in great danger?

(viii) What civilisation did Cortés conquer?

(ix) What was the name given to Cortés and Francisco Pizarro?

## (b) Document 2

The following is an extract from a letter sent from a native Peruvian named Huaman Poma to the King of Spain in 1513.

*I, the author of this work, went out into the world among other people just as poor as myself. I wanted to compile a record for the benefit of Your Majesty and also the Indians. Leaving my house in my own town, I have worked for thirty years at this task. My first step was to dress myself in sackcloth so that I would really seem to be a poor man as I looked around at what the world had to show for itself . . . In consequence I was a witness of the way in which the Indians are robbed of their property and their wives and daughters . . .*

*'The Spaniards are past masters at robbery and seduction, but they go further and try to make horses or slaves out of our people. When they talk about taxpaying Indians, what they mean is slaves, and in face of such an attitude our people are unable to prosper. They are bearing a burden without any longer having an Inca to defend them. And the only person available to undertake their defence is Your Majesty.*

*'The fact is that the very people who are paid to cherish the Indians [the priests] are the ones who band themselves together to exploit and deceive them . . .*

*'At last I decided to return to my own home . . . After the thirty years of my travels I also found my town and my province laid waste and the houses of my people in alien hands. When I came back, I discovered my own kin in a near-naked state, acting as servants to common taxpaying Indians . . .*

(i) For whose benefit did the author write this account?

(ii) How long has he been writing this record?

(iii) How does he believe the native Indians are being treated? Give reasons for your answer.

(iv) What does the author state that the Spaniards are the 'past masters' of?

(v) Why are the Incas 'unable to prosper'?

(vi) Does he believe that the Catholic priests can help them? Use evidence from the document to support your answer.

(vii) In what state did the author find his 'own kin' on his return?

(viii) Do you think that this author is happy with the Spanish colonists? Give reasons for your answer using evidence from the document.

(ix) Why do you think he believes that the 'only person available to undertake' the defence of the Indians is the King of Spain?

(x) List two lasting consequences of the Spanish conquest of South America for the local and native tribes like the Incas.

## Question 3: SHORT-ANSWER QUESTIONS

(a) Explain the following terms:

(i) *Conquistador*
(ii) Longitude
(iii) Knot
(iv) Caravel
(v) Circumnavigation
(vi) Colony
(vii) *Padroas*
(viii) Fathom
(ix) *Portolan*
(x) Lateen
(xi) Clinker-built

(b) Match the following navigational terms (1-6) in Column A with the correct definitions (a-f) in Column B:

| Column A | Column B |
|---|---|
| 1 Quadrants | (a) Measurement of speed of a ship |
| 2 Knots | (b) Measured the latitude of a ship |
| 3 Fathom | (c) Recorded where harbours were located along the coast |
| 4 Logbook | (d) Also measured the latitude of a ship |
| 5 Astrolabe | (e) Measurement of the depth of the sea |
| 6 *Portolan* maps | (f) Recorded the speed, route and direction of the journey |

(c) Write a sentence explaining what role the following people had in the period of exploration and discovery:

(i) Henry the Navigator
(ii) Bartholomew Diaz
(iii) Vasco da Gama
(iv) Christopher Columbus
(v) Amerigo Vespucci
(vi) Ferdinand Magellan
(vii) Antonio Pigafetta
(viii) Sebastian del Cano
(ix) Hernando Cortés
(x) Francisco Pizarro

(d) Take the three types of ship: (i) Lateen (ii) Clinker-built (iii) Caravel. Describe them using the following headings:

(a) Country that first used it
(b) Sea in which it was used
(c) Type of sail
(d) Advantages

(e) Fill in the gaps: Rewrite the following sentences filling in the missing words.

(i) The trade route to India and China that brought spices, jewels and silks to Western Europe was called the G_____ S______ R_______.

(ii) Europeans used spices from the Spices Island (also known as the M_____________ ).

(iii) It was thought that there was a legendary Christian king somewhere in the east called P_____________ J_______.

(iv) S_____ was a common disease that sailors suffered from due to lack of vitamin C.

(v) Henry the N___________ established a n_______________ school at S______ in Portugal.

(vi) Bartholomew Diaz named the most southerly point of Africa the C_____ of S______ but King John II renamed it as the C_________ of G________ H________.

(vii) Christopher Columbus first landed on the island of S___ S____________.

(viii) The Treaty of T_________________ agreed that Spain would own all lands west of a line drawn down the Atlantic Ocean.

(ix) Ferdinand Magellan found a route through to the P__________ Ocean by travelling through the M_____________ S _____________ .

(x) When del Cano arrived back to Seville in 1522 he had completed the first c _____________ of the world.

(xi) The ____________ civilisation existed in modern-day Mexico. Its capital was called T___________ and its king was called M____________.

(xii) The natives thought that Cortés was in fact a god called Q_____________.

(xiii) Mexico was renamed New __________ by Cortés and T_______________ was renamed Mexico City.

(xiv) Francisco Pizarro conquered the I_____ civilisation in Peru. The capital was called C_____ but Pizarro established a new capital at L______.

(f) Match the correct person in Column A with the location relevant to them in Column B:

| **Column A** | **Column B** |
|---|---|
| 1 Bartholomew Diaz | (a) America |
| 2 Vasco da Gama | (b) Inca Empire |
| 3 Christopher Columbus | (c) Aztec Empire |
| 4 Henry the Navigator | (d) Cape of Storms |
| 5 Hernando Cortés | (e) The Pacific Ocean |
| 6 Francisco Pizarro | (f) Sagres |
| 7 Ferdinand Magellan | (g) Hispaniola |
| 8 Amerigo Vespucci | (h) Natal |

## Question 4: PEOPLE IN HISTORY

**Imagine you are a sailor on board a voyage of exploration during the fifteenth and sixteenth centuries. Write an account of your life on board the ship.**

HINTS:

* The organisation of the voyage
* Life on board
* The voyage itself

Here are some bullet points about the voyage of Magellan to help you write an account of your life as a sailor.

### The Voyage Itself

- ➪ The size of the ship was very small and all the sailors had to sleep in very cramped places.
- ➪ There were great dangers at sea: unseen rocks or reefs could sink the ship and storms could sweep you overboard.
- ➪ Food was cooked in a firebox on deck but food often ran out. All the food had to be dried or salted to make sure it didn't go rotten. Water became putrid and all fresh fruit and vegetables rotted.
- ➪ The dirty water often caused typhoid and the lack of vitamin C resulted in an awful disease called scurvy which caused all our teeth to bleed and fall out.
- ➪ The ship's captain used *portolan* maps, astrolabes, compasses and quadrants to work out where we were and ropes with knots in them to measure the speed of the boat. All the details are written down by the captain in a logbook.

**OR**

**Write an account of a named leader of a voyage of discovery in the fifteenth or sixteenth centuries.**

HINTS:

* Early life
* Living conditions of sailors
* The voyage
* Later life

Here are some bullet points about Magellan to help you write an account of his voyage of discovery.

### Early Life of Ferdinand Magellan

- ➪ September 1519, Magellan sailed from Seville with 5 ships: the *Santiago*, *Victoria*, *Concepcion*, *San Antonio* and his flagship the *Trinidad*.
- ➪ Born into a noble family in Portugal in 1480.
- ➪ Sailed in a ship that travelled east to the Spice Islands. He was denied support for his journey to the Spice Islands by a westward route so he went to the Spanish King Charles V and was given funding.

### The Voyage

- ⇨ Sailed westward and then along the South American coastline. They wintered at a mouth of a river they called Rio de Janeiro (river of January). Later they moved south to Port St. Julian.
- ⇨ The Spanish captains, who were jealous of a Portuguese leader, mutinied. Magellan killed two mutineers and left one behind.
- ⇨ They travelled further south and saw a land with people with large feet and called it Patagonia. Finally they found a route through a strait at Cape Horn. There was an island that they passed that was snowcapped but had fires burning on it which they called Tierra del Fuego (Spanish for Land of Fire).
- ⇨ They passed through the straits into a very calm ocean which they named the Pacific (which means peaceful) Ocean. Magellan and the crew celebrated but then had to sail without any wind. The sailors ran out of food and water and many died of starvation and disease.

### Living condition of sailors

- ⇨ *See first answer* (The Voyage itself)

### Later Life

- ⇨ Eventually they came to the island of Guam in March 1521 but were attacked by the natives. They also discovered more islands which they called the Philippines after Prince Philip of Spain.
- ⇨ Magellan and his men were attacked by a tribe on the island of Mactan in the Philippines. Magellan was hit by a spear in the face and died.
- ⇨ Sebastian del Cano was able to bring the remaining ships back to Spain and by doing so completed the first circumnavigation of the world.

**OR**

**Imagine you are a native of a land that has been colonised by Europeans during the sixteenth century. Write an account of your life.**

HINTS:
- * The Civilisation
- * The Conquerors
- * The Colonisation
- * Consequences for the civilisation

Here are some bullet points about the Aztecs to help you write an account of your life as a native of land colonised by Europeans during the sixteenth century.

### The civilisation in question: The Aztecs

- ⇨ The Aztecs came from modern-day Mexico. They had a beautiful city called Tenochtitlan which was located on an island in the middle of a lake. It had canals that supplied fresh water to its 250,000 inhabitants.
- ⇨ The civilisation was very advanced and they could read and write. The Aztec religion demanded human sacrifice. They sacrificed people and animals to their god Quetzalcoatl who they believed had prophesised that he would return to them one day.

### The Conquistador: Hernando Cortés

- Cortés was living in Cuba when he took the opportunity to seek out the Aztec civilisation. He travelled with 500 soldiers and 16 horses and landed on the coast of Mexico in February 1519. He burnt his ships to show his men that there was no turning back.
- When the Aztecs saw Cortés on horseback, their king Montezuma thought he was the god Quetzalcoatl returning. They treated Cortés as a god but his men started to steal gold.
- The Aztecs threw Cortés and his men out and killed their king Montezuma.

### The conquering of the civilisation

- Cortés sought help from local tribes and returned in 1521 with an army of almost 100,000.
- Cortés captured Tenochtitlan and massacred the Aztecs. It was said that the lake was filled with the heads and bodies of Aztecs.
- The Aztec empire was renamed New Spain, Tenochtitlan was rebuilt as Mexico City and Cortés was made governor of the new lands.

### Consequences for the civilisation

- Spanish *conquistadores* continued to come and conquer new lands in South America including the Inca civilisation in Peru.
- In the process of seeking silver and gold, the Europeans forced the natives to work in mines and also imported African slaves.
- The new European diseases, the awful treatment and the forced work in the mines meant that almost all the native population of Mexico died over the next century.

## Question 5:

(a) Write a paragraph about two of the following topics:

(i) Spain's contribution to the Age of Exploration and Discovery

(ii) The Development of the caravel

(iii) Life at sea

(b) Give two positive and two negative consequences of the Age of Exploration and Discovery for either the native or the European populations.

Question 1: PICTURES

## (a) Picture A

(i) Name each of the reformers in A1, A2 and A3 above.

(ii) State where each of their reforms took place.

## (b) Picture B

(i) In picture B who is depicted in the top right-hand corner marked A?

(ii) What is he holding in his hands?

(iii) Who is sitting on the chair in the middle marked B?

(iv) Which of the two characters at A and B do you think the artist supports?

Give <u>two</u> reasons from the picture for your answer.

(v) Name <u>two</u> other reformers from this time.

## (c) Picture C

This map shows the religious divides in Europe after the Reformation. Examine the map and answer the questions that follow:

(i) What denominations were the populations of the areas marked A, B, C and D?

(ii) Name the religious reformers associated with the locations marked X, Y and Z.

(iii) Outline two consequences of the Reformation in Europe.

Study Documents **1** and **2** below, and then answer the questions that follow.

## (a) Document 1

The following is an extract from John Calvin's rules for the running of Geneva.

*Songs and Dances: If anyone sing songs that are unworthy, dissolute (immoral) or outrageous, or spin wildly round in the dance, or the like, he is to be imprisoned for three days, and then sent on to the consistory (a religious court).*

*Games: No one is to play at games that are dissolute, or at games played for gold or silver or at excessive expense, on pain of five sous (currency in Geneva) and loss of the sum staked.*

*Drunkenness:*

*There is to be no treating of one another to drinks, under penalty of three sous.*

*The taverns are to be closed during service, under penalty that the taverner pay three sous and anyone entering them the same.*

*If anyone be found drunk, he is to pay of the first time three sous and be brought before the consistory, the second time he must pay the sum of five sous, and the third ten sous and be put in prison.*

(i) What was the punishment for dancing 'wildly round' in a dance?

(ii) What type of games are banned?

(iii) What was the punishment for being caught playing these banned games?

(iv) When did the taverns have to close?

(v) What punishment did someone get if they were caught being drunk three times?

(vi) What is the name given to followers of Calvin?

(vii) Why was Geneva called the 'City of God'?

## (b) Document 2

The following is an extract from the autobiography of St. Ignatius de Loyola. He wrote the autobiography in the third person (as if he was describing someone else).

*Up to his twenty-sixth year he was a man given over to the vanities to the world and took a special delight in the exercise of arms [fighting], with a great and vain desire of winning glory.... [after being wounded in the war with France in 1521] he was not able to stand upon his leg, and so had to remain in bed. He had been much given to reading worldly books of fiction and knight errantry [adventures], and feeling well enough to read he asked for some of these books to help while away [pass] the time. In that house, however, they could find none of those he was accustomed [used] to read, and so they gave him a life of Christ and a book of the lives of the saints in Spanish. By the frequent reading of these books he conceived [imagined] some affection for what he found there narrated.*

(i) At what age was Ignatius injured in battle?

(ii) What were the books that he was accustomed to reading?

(iii) What books did he read instead?

(iv) What organisation did Ignatius later establish?
Give both the official name and the name by which its members are known

(v) Name a reform made by the Catholic Church as part of the Counter-Reformation.

## Question 3: SHORT-ANSWER QUESTIONS

(a) Explain the following terms:

| | | |
|---|---|---|
| (i) Reformation | (v) Nepotism | (ix) Jesuits |
| (ii) Absenteeism | (vi) Indulgences | (x) Vernacular |
| (iii) Pluralism | (vii) Theology | (xi) Presbyterian |
| (iv) Simony | (viii) Salvation | (xii) Anglican |

(b) Compare the Catholic and Lutheran religions under the following headings:

(i) Priests can marry or not
(ii) Number of sacraments
(iii) Language of service/mass and language of the Bible
(iv) How do you gain salvation?
(v) How do you find guidance about God?
(vi) Consubstantiation or Transubstantiation

(c) Write a sentence on what connection each of the following people had with the Reformation:

| | |
|---|---|
| (i) Albrecht of Mainz | (vii) Catherine of Aragon |
| (ii) John Tetzel | (viii) Anne Boleyn |
| (iii) Cardinal Cajetan | (ix) Thomas Cranmer |
| (iv) Frederick the Wise | (x) Queen Mary of England |
| (v) Philipp Melanchthon | (xi) Elizabeth I of England |
| (vi) John Knox | |

(d) Fill in the gaps: Rewrite the following sentences and fill in the missing words.

(i) The annual tax of 10% on the harvest of all the farmers was called the ____________.
(ii) ____________ was the place where people's souls went when they died so that their souls could be cleansed.
(iii) The clergy took vows of ____________. This meant that they would not marry.
(iv) Martin Luther was born in S ____________ in Germany. He believed in J ____________ B ____________ F ____________ A ____________.
(v) John T ____________ came to S ____________ to sell i ____________.
(vi) Luther nailed ____________ theses on the church door of ____________ castle.
(vii) Pope ____________ X threatened to excommunicate Luther.

(viii) Luther publicly burnt the P ____________ B ____________ that the Pope sent to him.

(ix) Luther attended a large meeting organised by Charles V of ____________ called the D ____________ of W ____________.

(x) Luther spent a year in ____________ Castle with Prince ____________ of Saxony.

(xi) P ____________ ____________ helped Luther to translate the Bible into German.

(xii) An outline of Luther's beliefs was published and called the C ____________ of A ____________.

(xiii) John Calvin wrote The I ____________ of the ____________ ____________.

(xiv) Calvin believed that people going to heaven were known as the 'e ____________'.

(xv) Geneva was known as the 'C ____________ of ____________'.

(xvi) The treaty that gave Huguenots equality in France with Catholics was called the ____________ of ____________.

(xvii) Henry VIII divorced ____________ of ____________ to be able to marry ____________ ____________.

(xviii) The Act of ____________ in 1534 recognised Henry VIII as supreme head of the Church of ____________.

(xix) Edward VI's reforms were known as the 42 ____________.

(xx) Elizabeth established the ____________ Church.

(xxi) The Catholic Church's reforms were known as the ____________ R ____________.

(xxii) The Society of Jesus was set up by St. ____________ of ____________

(e) Place the following women in chronological (time sequence) order, state what happened to them and give the names of any children they had:

(i) Catherine Howard

(ii) Anne of Cleves

(iii) Anne Boleyn

(iv) Catherine of Aragon

(v) Catherine Parr

(vi) Jane Seymour

(f) Match the following people (Column A) with the correct events (Column B) from the Reformation:

| **Column A** | **Column B** |
|---|---|
| 1 Elizabeth I of England | (a) Nailed 95 theses to Wittenberg Castle's church door |
| 2 John Calvin | (b) Established the Society of Jesus |
| 3 Henry VIII of England | (c) Called the Diet of Worms |
| 4 Martin Luther | (d) Established the Anglican Church |
| 5 John Knox | (e) Wrote The *Institutes of the Christian Religion* |
| 6 St. Ignatius of Loyola | (f) Helped Luther to translate the Bible into the vernacular |
| 7 Philipp Melanchthon | (g) Married Catherine of Aragon |
| 8 Charles V of Spain | (h) Spread Calvinism throughout Scotland |

(g) Find the following words in the wordsearch below.

| | | | | | |
|---|---|---|---|---|---|
| Reformation | Absenteeism | Pluralism | Simony | Indulgences | Predestination |
| Salvation | Vernacular | Worms | Presbyters | Huguenots | Consubstantiation |
| Auto-da-fe | Theology | Jesuits | Nepotism | Anglican | Excommunication |
| Transubstantiation | | | | | |

R E F O R M A T I O N X R T U N L P R
G J K L Q P R E D E S T I N A T I O N
M T R A N S U B S T A N T I A T I O N
Z Q U C N D A R A B S E N T E E I S M
M B F P R A U T O D A F E P K W N I S
P L U R A L I S M V E R P S N P D M R
I V E R N A C U L A R E O J R A U O E
M P H U G U E N O T S A T E L S L N T
T H E O L O G Y A S D G I S R W G Y Y
I Y P S I Q I O W O R M S U S A E P B
Q J E Y C P K L E S M C M I P T N N S
S A L V A T I O N W X O U T L H C O E
U I S I N D U L G E N C E S Y O E U R
C O N S U B S T A N T I A T I O N W P
J L K U E X C O M M U N I C A T I O N

## Question 4:
## PEOPLE IN HISTORY

**Using the following facts or hints, write an account of Martin Luther.**

HINTS: Remember to state his name.

* Early life
* Main events of his life
* Main beliefs of Lutheran Church
* Results of his life

### Martin Luther - Early Life

⇨ Born: Eisleben, Saxony in 1483.

⇨ Family: father was a copper miner.

⇨ Studied law at university of Erfurt.

⇨ Became an Augustinian monk and studied theology (the study of God, religion and religious beliefs) at Wittenberg, Germany.

⇨ Became Professor of Theology at Wittenberg.

### Main Events of his Life

⇨ Developed belief that faith alone was required for salvation. This was called Justification by Faith Alone.

⇨ Disagreed with John Tetzel's selling of indulgences in Saxony.

⇨ Pinned 95 theses (statements of opinion) on church door of castle of Wittenberg.

⇨ Pope Leo X sent Cardinal Cajetan to persuade Luther to take back his theses but Luther refused.

⇨ Pope Leo X sent a Papal Bull (letter) that threatened to excommunicate (expel) Luther from the Catholic Church which Luther publicly burnt.

⇨ Luther was invited to Diet of Worms to discuss problems. Luther attended but did not recant (take back) his objections so the Edict (order) of Worms made Luther a heretic.

⇨ Spent a year at Prince Frederick the Wise of Saxony's castle where he and Philipp Melanchthon translated the Bible into German.

⇨ Luther married Catherine von Bora in 1525.

⇨ In 1530, an outline of Luther's beliefs was published called the Confession of Augsburg.

⇨ Luther died in 1546.

### Main beliefs of Lutheran Church

- The Bible and not the pope was the only way to find out about God.
- Any member of the church could become a minister and any minister could marry.
- The Bible was translated into the vernacular (language of local population) so that people could read it.
- Believed in two sacraments rather than the seven that the Catholic Church believed in.
- Believed in consubstantiation.

### Results of his Life

- Northern Germany became Lutheran.
- Luther began what became known as the Protestant Reformation.
- Wars such as the Thirty Years War broke out between Protestants and Catholics.

**OR**

**Write an account of a follower of a religious reformer during the Reformation. You must state the reformer you are following. The start would be as follows:**

### Martin Luther

- 'I am a follower of Martin Luther. He was born in Eisleben, Saxony in 1483 to a copper miner. I met him first when he was studying to be a lawyer in Erfurt. I heard that he then studied theology at Wittenberg and became the professor there . . .'

## Question 5:

**Write a paragraph on <u>all</u> of the following topics:**

**(Give at least 6 points for each paragraph)**

**(a) The Reformation that occurred in England**

**(b) How Ireland was affected by the Reformation**

**(c) The Council of Trent and the Counter-Reformation**

**(d) Calvin's Geneva**

## (a) Picture A

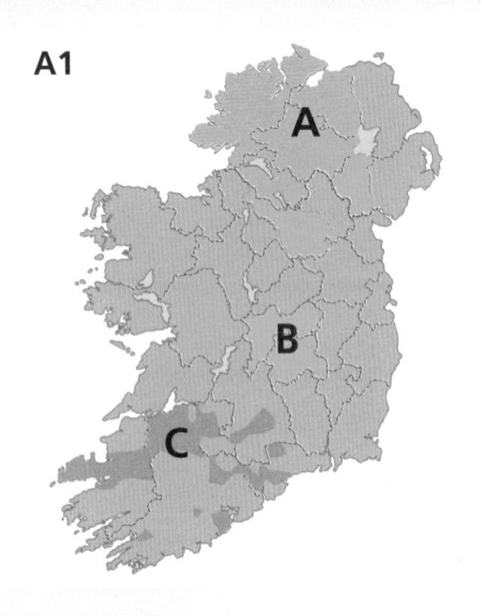


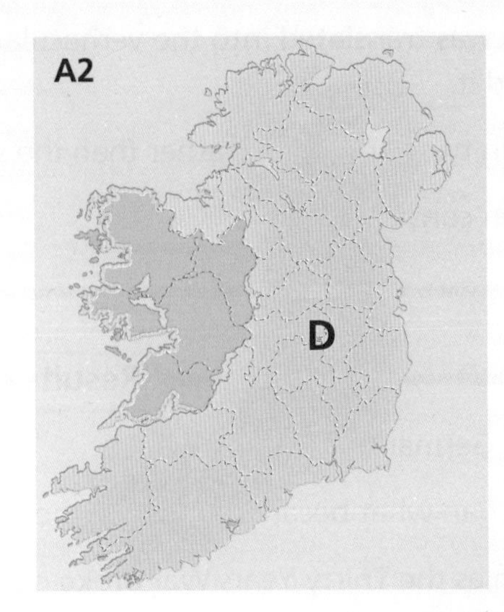


(i) State which plantations took place at locations A, B and C (A1) and D (A2).

(ii) Name the English leaders who were responsible for the plantations at A, B, C and D.

(iii) In your opinion which plantation was most successful? Give a reason for your answer.

## (b) Picture B

Examine Picture B which shows the O'Moore and O'Connor families attacking homes within the Pale and then answer the questions below.

(i) State which plantation this image is connected to.

(ii) What was the name given to the outlawed soldiers at A?

(iii) What are the people at B doing? Give a reason for your answer.

(iv) What are the soldiers at the top of the picture doing?

Study Documents **1** and **2** below, and then answer the questions that follow.

## (a) Document 1

This is an extract from an agreement made by MacGilpatrick of Upper Ossory with the King of England in the sixteenth century.

> 'First, the said MacGilpatrick doth utterly forsake and refuse the name [title] of MacGilpatrick; and all claim which he might pretend by the same; and promises to name himself, for ever hereafter, by such name as it shall please the King's Majesty to give him ... The said MacGilpatrick, his heirs and assignees and every other inhabiters of such lands as it shall please the King's Majesty to give onto him, shall use the English habits and manner, and, to their knowledge, the English language, and they, and every of them, shall to their power, bring up their children after the English manner, and the use of the English tongue.'

(i) What has the person named MacGilpatrick promised to 'forsake and refuse'?

(ii) What has MacGilpatrick promised to name himself?

(iii) On what land will MacGilpatrick, 'his heirs and assignees' live?

(iv) What other conditions must MacGilpatrick promise to follow?

(v) What was the name given to this process between the English King and the Irish lords and chieftains?

(vi) Name the King of England involved in this agreement.

## (b) Document 2

The following extract is from *Talamh Bánaithe (The Deserted Land)* written by Aindrias Mac Marcais around 1610.

*Tonight, Ireland is lonely. The banishment of her true chiefs causes the cheeks of her men and her fair women to be wet. It is strange that this people should be lonely . . . There is no laughter at children's doings, music is prohibited, the Irish language is in chains. Irish princes, unusually for them, speak not of wine-feasts nor mass. There is no playing, feasting, nor any pastime. There is no trading or riding horses or turning to face danger. No praise poem is recited, no bedtime story told, no desire to see a book, no giving ear to the family pedigrees . . . How shall the oppression be lifted from the bright fair-headed race of Conn, since we have no Moses in Ireland? There is none of them [Irish princes] who can lift her up after they have gone. The fact that the royal lines are under heavy oppression is stealing our soul from us.*

(i) Why are the men and women of Ireland crying?

(ii) List three ways that we can tell that Ireland is sad.

(iii) Why do you think that 'the Irish Language is in chains'?

(iv) What oppression do you think the author is referring to when he asks, 'how shall the oppression be lifted from the bright fair-headed race of Conn'?

(v) What event is the author referring to in this piece?

(vi) After which plantation did this event occur?

## Question 3: SHORT-ANSWER QUESTIONS

(a) Explain the following terms:

(i) The Pale
(ii) Surrender and Regrant
(iii) Plantation
(iv) Woodkernes
(v) Adventurers
(vi) Undertakers
(vii) Succession
(viii) Servitors

(b) Write a sentence explaining what connection the following had to the plantations in Ireland:

(i) Henry VIII
(ii) Earl of Desmond
(iii) James Fitzmaurice Fitzgerald
(iv) Sir Walter Raleigh
(v) Hugh O'Neill
(vi) Red Hugh O'Donnell
(vii) King Charles I
(viii) Oliver Cromwell
(ix) William Petty

(c) Fill in the gaps: Rewrite the following sentences and fill in the missing words:

(i) The area around Dublin, north as far as Dundalk and south as far as Ballymore Eustace where most of the English lived, was known as the __________ .

(ii) The three groups that made up Ireland in the early 1500s were the O __________ E __________, the Gaelicised Anglo-N __________ and the G __________ Irish.

(iii) Henry VIII proposed that the Gaelic Irish would recognise him as King of Ireland and swear an O __________ of S __________. In return he would give the Irish their land back and also an English peerage. This was called S __________ and R __________.

(iv) County Laois was renamed __________ County and Offaly was renamed __________ County. Furthermore, Portlaoise was renamed M __________ and Daingean was renamed P __________.

(v) W __________ were Gaelic outlaws who lived in the woods and attacked the Pale.

(vi) Queen Elizabeth encouraged Protestant Englishmen called a__________ to travel to Ireland and lay claim to land.

(vii) 600 troops sent by the Pope arrived in S __________ harbour, County K __________ in 1580.

(viii) The Fitzgeralds in Munster were known as the Earls of D __________.

(ix) The planters who promised to uphold the English crown's conditions were known as u__________.

(x) In 1582, Hugh O'Neill was appointed as E __________ of T __________ by Queen Elizabeth I.

(xi) In 1598, O'Neill and O'Donnell defeated the English army at Y __________ F __________.

(xii) After the defeat of the Irish troops at K __________ in 1601 by the English army, O'Neill signed the T __________ of M __________.

(xiii) In 1607, O'Neill and many of the other Gaelic leaders fled Ireland in what became known as the F __________ of the E __________.

(xiv) S __________ were soldiers who had served in the English army and who were now offered land as part of the Ulster Plantation.

(xv) The English Parliamentary army were known as the N __________ __________ Army and the soldiers were called r __________.

(xvi) Cromwell employed William P __________ to survey the island of Ireland. The details were known as the D __________ S __________.

(d) Match the people in Column A with the events in Column B.

| Column A | Column B |
|---|---|
| 1 Earl of Desmond | (a) Laois-Offaly plantation |
| 2 Hugh O'Neill | (b) Munster Plantation |
| 3 Oliver Cromwell | (c) Ulster Plantation |
| 4 Queen Mary of England | (d) Cromwellian Plantation |
| 5 William Petty | (e) The Nine Years War |
| 6 London Craft Guild | (f) Catholic Confederacy |

(e) Find the following words in the wordsearch below:

| | | | | |
|---|---|---|---|---|
| Pale | Adventurers | Servitors | Roundheads | Surrender and Regrant |
| Plantations | Undertakers | Mellifont | Hugh O'Neill | |
| Woodkernes | Succession | Yellow Ford | Cromwell | |

| P | A | L | E | M | S | F | R | S | P | W | P | O | Y | Q | R | N | M | S |
|---|---|---|---|---|---|---|---|---|---|---|---|---|---|---|---|---|---|---|
| A | D | W | G | V | D | C | G | K | L | D | U | I | E | H | L | D | Q | W |
| L | V | R | I | C | K | R | S | F | A | K | N | M | L | F | E | S | H | F |
| M | E | L | L | I | F | O | N | T | N | S | D | D | L | H | T | U | B | R |
| S | N | F | P | R | C | M | D | V | T | R | E | H | O | U | F | C | L | A |
| D | T | N | Z | L | X | W | L | B | A | O | R | U | W | G | D | C | H | K |
| R | U | J | X | D | Z | E | K | F | T | U | T | P | F | H | L | E | V | L |
| S | R | K | H | F | Q | L | O | S | I | N | A | W | O | O | H | S | W | M |
| H | E | U | K | J | K | L | W | O | O | D | K | E | R | N | E | S | Q | L |
| O | R | R | F | N | H | D | F | J | N | H | E | Q | D | E | H | I | D | N |
| L | S | E | R | V | I | T | O | R | S | E | R | A | S | I | D | O | B | O |
| W | L | O | F | U | H | S | F | D | R | A | S | G | A | L | A | N | G | F |
| L | M | B | F | H | J | C | A | W | L | D | P | O | D | L | D | Q | C | N |
| W | B | Z | D | J | O | V | E | H | E | S | L | A | J | D | A | F | V | B |
| S | U | R | R | E | N | D | E | R | A | N | D | R | E | G | R | A | N | T |

**Imagine you are a settler in a plantation in Ireland during the sixteenth or seventeenth centuries.**

**OR**

**Imagine you are an Irish landowner who has lost land during a plantation.**

In both cases, use the following facts or hints, to help you write an account of the Ulster Plantation. (Remember to state which plantation you are choosing)

HINTS:

* Reasons for the Plantations
* Where the planters came from
* People who received or lost land
* Results of the Plantation

## The Reasons for the Plantation

- Queen Elizabeth I of England and the Lord Deputy Fitzwilliam encouraged adventurers to lay claim to land in Ulster. They also imposed sheriffs to spread English law throughout Ulster.
- Hugh O'Neill and Red Hugh O'Donnell became very nervous about their positions.
- O'Donnell and the Archbishop of Armagh tried to persuade King Philip of Spain to help save Ulster from Protestantism but Philip refused.
- The Ulster Gaelic leaders joined together and O'Neill employed Scottish mercenaries called Gallowglasses, which means foreign warrior in Irish. This was the start of the Nine Years War (1594-1603).
- In 1598 the Ulster forces defeated an English force at Yellow Ford. The Spanish King Philip then changed his mind and sent 3,500 troops to Ireland and they landed in Kinsale, County Cork. The Ulster leaders decided to travel south to join up with them.
- They fought an unsuccessful battle against the English on Christmas Eve, 1601. O'Neill then escaped before finally surrendering and signed the Treaty of Mellifont in 1603. O'Neill and many other Gaelic leaders finally left Ireland entirely in 1607 in what became known as the Flight of the Earls.

## The people who received or lost land

- Gaelic leaders who fought with O'Neill and then had their land confiscated under the rules of Surrender and Regrant.
- Gaelic leaders who fled Ireland in 1607 and so lost their lands.
- Servitors who had fought with the English Army and were given land as a reward for 'serving'.
- English people who had 'undertaken' to live by the rules of the plantation.
- Members of the London Craft Guild who moved to Derry to create new industries.

### Where the planters came from

- Undertakers came from either England or Scotland,
- Servitors came from England in particular.
- The London Craft Guild around Derry all came from London.

### The results of the plantation

- By 1640 there were 40,000 Scots in Ulster.
- Religious tensions grew between Scottish Presbyterians, English Anglicans and the Gaelic Catholics who had lost land.
- New industries began in areas around the city of Derry (which was renamed Londonderry).

## Question 5:

**(a) Write a paragraph about two of the following:**

**(Give at least 5 points for each paragraph.)**

**(i) The Laois-Offaly Plantation**

**(ii) The Munster Plantation**

**(iii) The Ulster Plantation**

**(iv) The Cromwellian Plantation**

**(b) Write a paragraph on the lasting effects (if any) that the plantations had on the island of Ireland. Give two reasons to support your answer.**

## Question I: PICTURES

### (a) Picture A

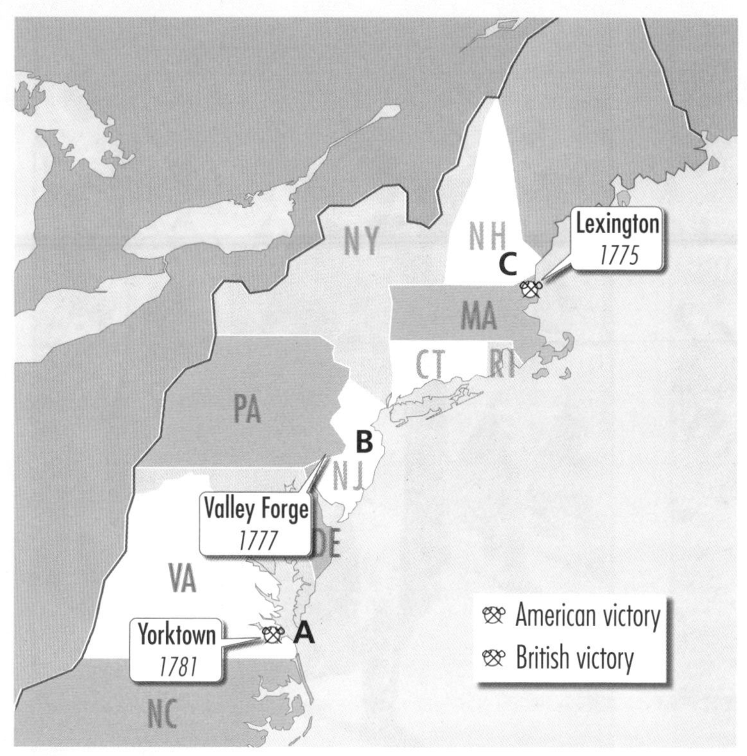


(i) Name the leaders of the American and British armies who fought the battle of Yorktown, marked A, and state who won.

(ii) Name three of the original American colonies

(iii) The American army wintered at Valley Forge, marked B. Who was the German army leader who gave help to the American troops there?

(iv) The battle of Lexington, marked C, was one of the first battles of the American War of Independence. Who rode through the night to warn the inhabitants?

(v) Give two reasons why the American army was able to defeat the British army.

### (b) Picture B

*'Tithes, Taxes and Graft'*

(i) What do each of the three characters in this cartoon from the French Revolution represent?

(ii) What is the relevance of the title of the cartoon?

(iii) What do you think the cartoon is trying to say?

## (c) Picture C

Picture A is of Henry Joy McCracken during the 1798 Uprising. Picture B shows Robert Emmet at his rising in 1803. Examine both pictures and answer the questions that follow:

(i) Identify the main weapons used by the rebels in both pictures.

(ii) Do you think that the artist of Picture A is for the rising or against it? Give two reasons for your answer using evidence from the picture.

(iii) Name another leader of the Ulster rising.

(iv) What happened to a) Henry Joy McCracken and b) Robert Emmet?

(v) In your opinion, why did the 1798 Uprising fail? Give two reasons and use evidence or examples to back up your reasons.

Study Documents **1, 2** and **3** below, and then answer the questions that follow.

## (a) Document 1

Read the following extract from Thomas Paine's written account of the winter in Valley Forge (1777-1778) during the American War of Independence:

These are the times that try men's souls. The summer soldier and the sunshine patriot will, in this crisis, shrink from the service of their country; but he that stands by it now, deserves the love and thanks of man and woman. Tyranny, like hell, is not easily conquered; yet we have this consolation with us, that the harder the conflict, the more glorious the triumph. What we obtain too cheap, we esteem too lightly: it is dearness only that gives every thing its value. Heaven knows how to put a proper price upon its goods; and it would be strange indeed if so celestial an article as freedom should not be highly rated. Britain, with an army to enforce her tyranny, has declared that she has a right (not only to tax) but "to bind us in all cases whatsoever" and if being bound in that manner, is not slavery, then is there not such a thing as slavery upon earth. Even the expression is impious; for so unlimited a power can belong only to God.

(i) Does Paine admire the 'summer soldier and the sunshine patriot'?

(ii) Who does Paine believe 'deserves the love and thanks of man and woman'?

(iii) Why does he think that freedom should be 'so highly rated'?

(iv) Name the two rights Britain claims to have over America.

(v) Who only could have 'so unlimited a power'?

(vi) Is the author a supporter of the Americans? Give two reasons from the text to support your answer.

(vii) Name another well-known pamphlet that Thomas Paine wrote.

## (b) Document 2

Read the following extract from a letter by Philippe Pinel which describes the execution of King Louis XVI of France on 21 January 1793:

Louis, who, fortified by the principles of religion, seemed completely resigned to meet death, left his prison in the Temple about nine in the morning and was taken to the place of execution in the mayor's carriage with his confessor and two gendarmes, the curtains being drawn.

When he arrived at his destination he looked at the scaffold without flinching. The executioner at once proceeded to perform the customary rite by cutting off the King's hair which he put in his pocket. Louis then walked up onto the scaffold. The air was filled with the roll of numerous drums, seemingly intended to prevent the people from demanding grace. The drumbeats were hushed for a moment by a gesture from Louis himself, but at a signal from the adjutant of the General of the National Guard, they recommenced with such force that Louis's voice was drowned and it was only possible to catch a few stray words like "I forgive my enemies." At the same time he took a few steps round the fatal plank to which he was drawn by a feeling of horror natural to any man on the brink of death or, maybe, he conceived that the people might appeal for grace, for what man does not cling to hope even in his last moments?

The adjutant ordered the executioner to do his duty and in a trice Louis was fastened onto the deadly plank of the machine they call the guillotine and his head was cut off so quickly that he could hardly have suffered. This at least is a merit belonging to the murderous instrument which bears the name of the doctor who invented it. The executioner immediately lifted the head from the sack into which it fell automatically and displayed it to the people.

As soon as the execution had taken place, the expression on the faces of many spectators changed and, from having worn an air of sombre consternation, they shifted to another mood and fell to crying, "Vive la Nation!" At least one can say this of the cavalry who witnessed the execution and who waved their helmets on the point of their sabres.

Some of the citizens followed suit, but a great number withdrew, their spirits racked with pain, to shed tears in the bosom of their families.

(i) How can we tell that Louis was not scared?

(ii) What 'customary rite' did the executioner perform?

(iii) What were Louis' last words?

(iv) What does the author believe is a merit of the guillotine?

(v) How can we tell that some of the crowd were happy that Louis had been executed?

(vi) Was everyone happy that Louis had been executed? Give reasons for your answer using evidence from the text.

(vii) Do you think the author admired the King? Give reasons for your answer using evidence from the text.

## (c) Document 3

This is an extract from the diary of Theobald Wolfe Tone written in 1796.

*December 22nd*
*This morning, at eight, we have neared Bantry Bay considerably, but the fleet is scattered . . . I am so happy as to arrive there. We are gaining the Bay by slow degrees, with a head wind at east where it has hung these five weeks. Tonight we hope, if nothing extraordinary happens, to cast anchor in the mouth of the Bay, and work up tomorrow morning; these delays are dreadful to my impatience, I am now so near the shore that I can see, distinctly, two old castles, yet I am utterly uncertain whether I shall ever set foot on it.*

*December 23rd*
*Last night it blew a heavy gale from the eastward with snow, so that the mountains are covered this morning . . . We lie in this disorder, expecting a visit from the English every hour, without taking a single step for our defence, even to the common one of having a frigate in the harbour's mouth, to give us notice of their approach . . . I am now so near the shore that I can in a manner touch the sides of Bantry Bay with my right and left and yet God knows whether I shall ever tread again on Irish ground . . . I could tear my flesh with rage and vexation, but that advances nothing, and so I hold my tongue in general and devour my melancholy as I can. To come so near, and then to fail, if we are to fail! And everyone aboard seems now to have given up all hopes.*

*December 29th*
*At four this morning the Commodore made the signal to steer for France; so there is an end of our expedition for the present; perhaps for ever. I spent all yesterday in my hammock, partly through sea-sickness and much more through vexation . . .*

*December 30th/31st*
*On our way to Brest. It will be well supposed I am in no great humour to make memorandums. This is the last day of the year 1796, which has been a very remarkable one in my history.*

(i) What problem is stopping Wolfe Tone from landing at Bantry Bay?

(ii) What does Wolfe Tone expect will happen if the fleet continues to anchor in the bay without landing?

(iii) In what way does Wolfe Tone show just how close he is to land? Give two examples.

(iv) Is Wolfe Tone upset about not reaching land? Give reasons using evidence from the text to support your answer.

(v) Why did Wolfe Tone not write much in his diary on 30 and 31 December 1796?

(vi) In 1798, Wolfe Tone tried to sail into Ireland again. Where did that occur?

(vii) How did Wolfe Tone die?

## Question 3: SHORT-ANSWER QUESTIONS

(a) Explain the following terms:

(i) Townshend Acts
(ii) Tea Act
(iii) Boston tea party
(iv) Democracy
(v) *Ancien regime*
(vi) Bourgeoisie
(vii) Sans-culottes
(viii) Reign of Terror
(ix) Protestant Ascendancy
(x) Catholic Emancipation
(xi) Act of Union (1801)
(xii) Cat o' nine tails

(b) Match the following events in Column A with the correct revolution in Column B:

| Column A | Column B |
|---|---|
| 1 Battle of Vinegar Hill | (a) American War of Independence |
| 2 Battle of Ballynahinch | (b) French Revolution |
| 3 Battle of Saratoga | (c) 1798 Uprising |
| 4 Fall of the Bastille | |
| 5 Battle of White Plains | |
| 6 Races of Castlebar | |
| 7 Flight to Varennes | |
| 8 Reign of Terror | |
| 9 Battle of Philadelphia | |

(c) Place the following events in the correct chronological (time sequence) order:

(i) Fall of the Bastille
(ii) Reign of Terror
(iii) Creation of the National Assembly
(iv) Committee of Public Safety
(v) Napoleon Bonaparte as Emperor
(vi) The Tennis Court Oath
(vii) The Estates General
(viii) Declaration of the Rights of Man
(ix) Flight to Varennes
(x) Law of Maximum
(xi) Execution of Louis XVI

(d) Write a sentence about each of the following people:

(i) Paul Revere
(ii) Frederick von Steuben
(iii) Thomas Jefferson
(iv) Queen Marie-Antoinette
(v) The sans-culottes
(vi) Marquis de Lafayette
(vii) Maximilien Robespierre
(viii) General Hoche
(ix) Theobald Wolfe Tone
(x) General Lake
(xi) Lord Edward Fitzgerald
(xii) Henry Joy McCracken

(e) Fill in the gaps: Rewrite the following sentences and fill in the missing words:

(i) The S________ Act (1765) placed a tax on all official documents such as wills and public documents such as newspapers for all American colonists.

(ii) In March 1770, five protestors were shot and seven others injured by British troops in what became known as the B___________ M___________.

(iii) American colonists disguised themselves as American Indians, boarded a ship and dumped its cargo of 45 tonnes of tea into the sea. This event became known as the B________ __________ __________.

(iv) Thomas J__________ wrote the American Declaration of I____________.

(v) George Washington was made the commander of the newly created A__________ C__________ Army in 1775.

(vi) The British General C______________ surrendered to W_______________ after the battle of Y__________ in 1781.

(vii) America gained its independence after signing the T______ of V_________ in 1783.

(viii) To organise the raising of taxes, Louis XVI called the E_______-G________ in 1789.

(ix) The Third E_______ left the E_____-G______ and promised not to give up until they had achieved a constitution for France that took account of their grievances. This promise was called the T_____ C_____ O_______.

(x) The ______________ was a large prison in the middle of Paris.

(xi) King Louis and Marie-Antoinette tried to flee France but were caught at V________

(xii) Robespierre was the leader of the Committee of _______________ ____________.

(xiii) Within one year during 1793-1794, it is thought over 40,000 people were executed during the R_____ of T_________.

(xiv) Wolfe Tone, among others, established the Society of the U_______ I__________ in 1791.

(xv) In 1796 W_____ T________ and the French General Hoche tried to land 43 ships with 15,000 troops at B_______ Bay but storms made it impossible.

(xvi) Uprisings took place in W_________, in U_______ and also in County Mayo throughout 1798.

(xvii) Daniel O'Connell achieved Catholic E___________ and was known as The L_______.

(d) Match the people in Column A with the relevant event in Column B:

| Column A | Column B |
|---|---|
| 1 Henry Joy McCracken | (a) Castlebar Races |
| 2 Bagenal Harvey | (b) Battle of Antrim |
| 3 General Hoche | (c) Reign of Terror |
| 4 General Humbert | (d) Valley Forge |
| 5 Frederick von Steuben | (e) Wexford Rising |
| 6 Maximilien Robespierre | (f) Bantry Bay |

## Question 4:
## PEOPLE IN HISTORY

**(a) Write about a named revolutionary leader in America during the late eighteenth century.**

**Name: George Washington.**

**(Note: Use either 'he' or 'I' when writing.) You may use the following hints to help you.**

HINTS:

* Early life
* War of Independence
* End of War

### Early Life

⇨ Born in Westmoreland County, Virginia in 1732 and became a wealthy landowner.

⇨ Fought with the British against the French in the Seven Years War. He returned to Virginia where he married a wealthy widow named Martha Dandridge.

⇨ He was elected as Virginia's representative at the First and the Second Continental Congress.

⇨ Made leader of the newly formed American Continental Army and had to organise all the colonists who were farmers and tradesmen and had very little military experience or equipment. However, the colonists knew the land better than the British and were very determined to fight for their homes.

### The War of Independence

⇨ After capturing Boston, the Americans lost New York and were defeated at White Plains in 1776.

⇨ Two small victories at Princeton and Trenton were achieved before being forced out of Philadelphia in September 1777.

⇨ The American General Gates managed to gain a victory at Saratoga and he captured 8,000 British troops.

⇨ This victory and the help of the French, Spanish and Dutch began to turn the war in the Americans' favour. The French navy was particularly important.

⇨ The winter of 1777-1778 in Valley Forge was really difficult. Food and supplies were short and over 2,000 soldiers died from cold and disease. A Prussian army officer from Germany called Frederick von Steuben helped to teach the soldiers and made them a more disciplined army. Washington endeared himself to his troops by remaining in the camp and suffering the conditions alongside his men.

⇨ Over the next year, the Americans slowly took control of the war and in October 1781 Washington managed to trap the British General Cornwallis between his army and the French navy at Yorktown.

### End of War

- In 1783, the British signed a peace treaty at Versailles, near Paris which recognised American independence.
- Washington returned back to his estate in Virginia but was asked to become the first President of the newly formed United States of America in 1789. He moved to the new capital of the District of Columbia and oversaw the building of the White House although he was the only American president not to live in it.
- He was re-elected in 1793 for a second term and finally retired fully in 1797.
- Washington died in Virginia in 1799.

**(b) Write about a named revolutionary leader from Ireland in the late eighteenth century.**

**OR**

**Write an account of a supporter of a named revolutionary leader in the late eighteenth century.**

**Name: Theobald Wolfe Tone.**

**(Note: Use either 'I' or 'he' in the account.) You may use the following hints to help you.**

HINTS:

* Reasons for becoming a revolutionary
* Revolutionary activities
* Political activities

### Reasons for becoming a revolutionary

- The Penal Laws in the eighteenth century discriminated against Catholics and to a lesser extent Presbyterians, e.g. Catholics could not become solicitors, judges or barristers, they could not build or attend schools or churches, no priests were allowed to stay in Ireland and all land had to be subdivided among all sons in a family making it very difficult to produce enough food for the families. Even though Catholics made up 75% of Ireland's population, they owned less than 15% of the land.
- Members of the Anglican Church (Church of Ireland) made up only 15% of the population but owned almost all the land in Ireland and had all the political power.
- The Presbyterians (Dissenters) were mainly in Ulster and were banned from being elected to Parliament or holding positions of power.
- The Navigation Acts placed restrictions on Irish exports of cattle and wool which caused great economic difficulties for Irish industries.

## Political Activities

- Wolfe Tone was born into an Anglican family in Dublin in 1763 and studied law at Trinity College. He was inspired by the French Revolution and believed that there was a great need for political reform.
- In August 1791 he published *An Argument on Behalf of the Catholics of Ireland.*
- Along with Henry Joy McCracken, Samuel Nielson and Thomas Russell he established the Society of the United Irishmen in October 1791. The United Irishmen wished for complete independence and radical political reform.
- He was asked to work for the Catholic Committee to gain Catholic emancipation and the committee managed to gain the Catholic right to vote but not the right to sit in parliament. Wolfe Tone believed that violence was necessary to achieve full independence for Ireland.

## Revolutionary Activities

- In 1795, Wolfe Tone was forced to go into exile to America after a French spy named William Jackson was caught in Ireland gathering information from Wolfe Tone
- Wolfe Tone went to France to seek support for a rebellion in 1796.
- In December 1796, Wolfe Tone and 43 ships with 15,000 French troops set sail for Ireland under the command of General Hoche. The ships were hit by a storm before they could land at Bantry Bay in County Cork. After losing a number of ships, the French troops returned to France.
- The British then sent General Lake to use brutal methods like pitch-capping and the walking gallows to put down any rebellion. They also captured one of the main leaders Lord Edward Fitzgerald who later died from wounds he received during his arrest.
- The Uprising took place in Wexford led by Father John Murphy and a Protestant landowner named Bagenal Harvey. They captured Enniscorthy and Wexford Town but were defeated finally at Vinegar Hill.
- In Ulster, Henry Joy McCracken and Henry Munro led the Uprising in Antrim and Ballynahinch but were defeated. The two leaders were caught and beheaded.
- In August 1798, 1,000 French troops arrived in Killala in Mayo under General Humbert. They captured Ballina and then Castlebar before General Lake and Cornwallis defeated the French army at Ballinamuck, County Longford.
- Wolfe Tone sailed to Ireland in October with 3,000 more French troops but they were met at Lough Swilly by a British fleet and defeated at sea. Wolfe Tone was captured, found guilty of treason and sentenced to be hanged.
- Wolfe Tone attempted to kill himself with a pen knife while in prison but only succeeded in injuring himself. He died a week later from the injury on 19 November 1798.

## Question 5:

(a) Write a paragraph on two of the following topics:

(i) French assistance for the Irish Rising of 1798

(ii) The influence of the American and French Revolutions on the 1798 Rising in Ireland

(iii) The lasting consequences of the Revolutions in America and France

(b) Write a paragraph about the period in the French Revolution called the Reign of Terror.

(c) In your opinion, was the French Revolution a good thing or a bad thing? Give two reasons using evidence from your studies to support your answer.

## (a) Picture A

**Examine Picture A above and answer the following questions:**

(i) What form of transport is depicted on the bridge at the top of this picture?

(ii) What type of goods were transported in this way during the Industrial Revolution?

(iii) Give one advantage and one disadvantage of this method of transportation.

(iv) What form of transportation replaced this one as the main method of transporting goods during the Industrial Revolution?

(v) Name another method of transporting heavy goods that existed at this time.

## (b) Picture B

**Examine Picture B and answer the following questions:**

(i) What product is being manufactured in this picture?

(ii) Name two machines that would have been used to manufacture the product during the Industrial Revolution.

(iii) Give a description of the conditions for workers in factories such as this one during the 1800s.

(iv) Name two dangers that workers faced in a factory such as this one.

Study Documents **1** and **2** below, and then answer the questions that follow.

## (a) Document 1

This is an extract from Friedrich Engels' *Condition of the Working Class* from 1845, after his visit to Manchester in 1842. In this extract he describes the area in Manchester known as 'Little Ireland'.

> *In a rather deep hole, in a curve of the Medlock [canal] and surrounded on all four sides by tall factories and high embankments covered with buildings, stand two groups of about two hundred cottages, built chiefly back to back, in which live about four thousand human beings, most of them Irish. The cottages are old, dirty and of the smallest sort, the streets uneven, fallen into ruts and in part without drains or pavement; masses of refuse, offal [insides of animals] and sickening filth lie among standing pools in all directions; the atmosphere is poisoned by effluvia [smells or fumes] from these, and laden and darkened by the smoke of a dozen tall factory chimneys. A horde of ragged women and children swarm here, as filthy as the swine that thrive upon the garbage heaps and in the puddles.*

(i) Where are the two groups of cottages where the Irish live?

(ii) How are the cottages described?

(iii) Give a description of the streets.

(iv) What sorts of diseases were common in slums like the one described in this extract, during the Industrial Revolution? Name two.

(v) From this extract, name two causes of disease which were present in 'Little Ireland'.

(vi) What is the name given to areas in cities like the one described here?

## (b) Document 2

The following extract is from a report on the Irish Famine by Joseph Crosfield in *Transactions of the Central Relief Committee of the Society of Friends 1846 and 1847.*

At this place our first visit was to the poorhouse; and as the board of guardians was then sitting for the admission of applicants, a most painful and heartrending scene presented itself; poor wretches in the last stage of famine, imploring to be received into the house; women who had six or seven children begging that even two or three of them might be taken in, as their husbands were earning but 8d per day; which at the present high price of provisions, was totally inadequate to feed them. Some of these children were worn to skeletons, their features sharpened with hunger, and their limbs wasted almost to the bone.

From a number of painful cases, the following may be selected. A widow with two children, who for a week had subsisted on one meal of cabbage each day; these were admitted into the poorhouse, but in so reduced a state that a guardian observed to the master of the house that the youngest child would trouble them but a very short time.

Another woman with two children, and near her confinement again, whose husband had left her a month before to seek for work, stated that they had lived for the whole of this week upon two quarts of meal and two heads of cabbage. Famine was written in the faces of this woman and her children. In reply to a question from William Forster [the English Quaker], the guardians expressed their opinion that these statements were true. Of course, among so many applicants as there were in attendance (one hundred and ten), a great number were necessarily refused admittance, as there were but thirty vacancies in the house.

The guardians appeared to exercise great discrimination and impartiality in the selection of the most destitute objects; but some of those who were rejected were so far spent, that it is doubtful if them would all reach their homes alive, as several of them had to walk five or six Irish miles.

(i) What event was taking place when the author arrived at the poorhouse?

(ii) Give the description used in the report of the starving children. Do you think it is a good description? Give reasons for your answer.

(iii) How can we tell that the youngest child of the widow admitted into the poorhouse was very sick?

(iv) Why could all 110 applicants not be admitted into the poorhouse?

(v) Does the author think that the guardians were doing a good job or not? Use evidence from the document to support your answer.

(vi) Does the author have much hope for those people who were not admitted into the poorhouse? Give reasons for your answer.

(vii) This report was for the Central Relief Committee of the Society of Friends. Give another name for the 'Society of Friends'.

## Question 3: SHORT-ANSWER QUESTIONS

(a) Explain the following terms:

(i) Loom
(ii) Mill
(iii) Coke
(iv) Slum
(v) Puddling and rolling
(vi) Collier
(vii) Subsistence farmer
(viii) Cottier
(ix) Conacre
(x) Blight
(xi) Laissez-faire
(xii) Evictions
(xiii) Coffin ships
(xiv) Textile
(xv) Yarn
(xvi) Maize
(xvii) Workhouses

(b) Explain in two or three sentences who each of the following people are in relation to the nineteenth century in Ireland and Britain:

(i) Edward Jenner
(ii) Charles Townshend
(iii) Robert Bakewell
(iv) Jethro Tull
(v) Cyrus McCormick
(vi) John Kay
(vii) Richard Arkwright
(viii) Samuel Crompton
(ix) Edmund Cartwright
(x) James Watt
(xi) Abraham Darby
(xii) Henry Bessemer
(xiii) Thomas Telford
(xiv) John MacAdam
(xv) George Stevenson
(xvi) James Brindley
(xvii) Robert Owen
(xviii) Robert Peel

(c) (i) With regard to the following people, name the agricultural inventions or changes in agricultural methods with which they are associated.

(1) Charles Townshend, 1700s
(2) Robert Bakewell, 1700s
(3) Jethro Tull, 1701
(4) Cyrus McCormick, 1834

(ii) State the purpose of each of the four inventions or changes.

(d) (i) With regard to the following people, name the textile invention with which they are associated.

(1) John Kay, 1733
(2) James Hargreaves, 1764
(3) Richard Arkwright, 1769
(4) Samuel Crompton, 1779
(5) Edmund Cartwright, 1785

(ii) State the purpose of each of the five inventions.

(e) (i) With regard to the following five people, name the industrial invention or improvement with which they are associated.

(1) Thomas Newcomen, 1712
(2) James Watt, 1769
(3) Abraham Darby, 1709
(4) Henry Cort, 1790s
(5) Henry Bessemer, 1856

(ii) Some people believe that the steam engine was the most important invention of the Industrial Revolution. Do you agree? Give reasons for your answer.

(f) (i) With regard to the following five people, name the improvement in transport methods or transport invention with which they are associated.

(1) Thomas Telford, 1800s
(2) John MacAdam, 1800s
(3) James Brindley, 1761
(4) George Stevenson, 1830
(5) Isambard Kingdom Brunel, 1860

(ii) State the purpose of each of the five improvements or inventions.

(g) Fill in the gaps: Rewrite the following sentences and fill in the missing words:

(i) Edward J________ found the first v__________ for small pox by injecting someone with c____ pox.

(ii) Britain was lucky to have large deposits of both c______ and i______.

(iii) During the Agricultural Revolution, many farmers e__________ their land by putting hedges and fences around their fields.

(iv) Charles Townshend began to plant t_______ in his fields instead of leaving them fallow. This removed weeds and provided food for the animals during the winter. He also used c______ in his fields to provide nitrogen for the soil. This system was called the N______ C______ Rotation system.

(v) Robert B_______ only allowed his best animals to breed. This s___________ breeding meant his animals became much bigger.

(vi) Jethro T_____ invented the s______ d______ to plant each seed in neat lines and cover them with soil to stop birds from eating them.

(vii) Since the seeds were planted in neat lines, Cyrus M________ was able to invent the m_________ r_________ to harvest the crop.

(viii) Wool or fibres from plants such as c_____ or f______ were spun into y________. This y______ was then woven into t______ or cloth on a l_________.

(ix) Many inventions like the S________ Jenny, the W_____-F______ and the S_______ M______ helped spin the yarn. The Flying S________ and later the P_____ L_______ ensured that a vast amount of yarn was woven into t_______.

(x) Iron was made by heating the iron o____ in a furnace to remove impurities. This process is called s_________.

(xi) To make the iron purer, Henry C_____ invented the process of p________ and r_________.

(xii) Henry B_________ added m_________ to iron and forced air through the mixture in his c_________. This process produced a metal called s_______.

(xiii) Thomas T_____ and John M________ both made great improvements in road design.

(xiv) The B________________ Canal from Wosley to Manchester was designed by James _________.

(xv) George S____________'s R_______ was a locomotive that could go up to almost 50 kilometres an hour.

(xvi) C________ worked in mines digging c_____ from seams in the earth.

(xvii) Robert O_______ set up a cotton factory in New L________ in Scotland. This factory treated its workers well.

(xviii) Many tenant farmers in Ireland in the mid-1800s were only able to grow enough food to feed themselves. This is called s____________ farming.

(xix) Irish farm labourers were known as c_______. They rented a small area of land to grow their potatoes. This land was called a c________.

(xx) The Great F_______ was caused by potato b________ that attacked the tubers of the potato.

(xxi) The British Prime Minister, Robert P_______ had tonnes of Indian c_____ or m_______ imported to Ireland.

(xxii) Many tenants were unable to pay their rent and were e________ from their homes.

(xxiii) Many people left Ireland to go abroad on what were known as c______ ships.

## Question 4:
## PEOPLE IN HISTORY

**(a) Write an account of a worker in Britain during the Industrial Revolution using the following facts or hints. Choose either (i) a factory worker OR (ii) a miner.**

HINTS:

* Your daily life at work
* Your home and family
* Diseases
* Leisure time
* Improvements in working conditions

### Your daily life at work: (i) The factory worker

- ⇨ Started work in the factory at 5:30 in the morning and finished between 5:30 and 9:30 that evening. In total, worked 12-16 hours a day with only Sunday as a holiday.
- ⇨ The textile factory had very large and loud machines. Many people got injured using them. If they were not able to work, the owner got someone else to do the work.
- ⇨ The machines in this factory were called Power Looms and they turned yarn into cloth.
- ⇨ There were many jobs in the factory: spinners were in charge of the machines, piercers had to put the threads together if they broke and scavengers crawled under the machines, brushed the dust and kept the room clean.
- ⇨ There were many rules in the factory: no whistling, singing or bad language. If a machine broke, the workers had to pay for it. Workers were fined if they broke a rule or were late for work. Sometimes the children were beaten if they did not do their job correctly.
- ⇨ Workers were allowed 40 minutes for dinner and three toilet breaks a day.

### Your daily life at work: (ii) The miner

- ⇨ Miners worked for 14 hours a day in the mines.
- ⇨ From the age of five children worked as trappers. They opened and closed the doors in the shafts to stop the spread of dangerous gases.
- ⇨ At the age of eight, children became hurriers and pushed or pulled carts full of coal through the mines.
- ⇨ When they grew strong enough to become a collier, they would stand at the coalface and dig out the coal with a pickaxe.
- ⇨ The mine could easily collapse or flood. Newcomen's engine was used to pump the water out of the shafts.
- ⇨ Poisonous and flammable gases like methane could cause explosions in the mine. To avoid any naked flames in the mine, Davy's Safety Lamp was used from 1816. It covered the flame with a thin cloth called a gauze.
- ⇨ Miners suffered from misshapen backs from having to bend over all day. They also had poor eyesight from being in the dark for so long. Miner's Lung was a disease caused by the constant inhalation of coal dust.

## Your home and family

- In the evening the workers returned to their houses in the city. Whole families lived in single rooms of small houses.
- There was no running water or toilets in the house. Water could be found in the streams nearby but they were very dirty as people used them as a toilet.
- It was too expensive to heat the rooms, so people slept on straw on the cold damp ground.
- These houses were all built very close to each other and hundreds of families lived beside each other. The areas like this were called slums.
- The streets were dirty with rubbish and human waste.
- Everyone in the family, even the children, had to work to earn money to buy food.

## Diseases

- Due to the bad conditions in the workplace and at home there were many diseases.
- Typhoid and cholera were caused by drinking the dirty water.
- The dirty air caused by all the smoke created smog. This made people cough and causef asthma.
- Sleeping in damp and cold conditions, combined with a poor diet, caused tuberculosis.
- Smallpox and other infectious diseases spread very quickly throughout the slums.

## Leisure Time

- On Sundays the whole family had a day off.
- Many people spent all day in the pub and they used all their wages to get drunk in the gin houses and bars in the city.
- Others went to watch the cock- and dog-fighting and place bets on who would win.
- There were organised games of association football or rugby in the winter and cricket in the summer. Some people organised teams to play against each other.

### Improvements in working conditions

- The Chartists tried to get some improvements for workers but the parliament refused to listen to their demands.
- Some trade unions were created to help workers but many of the leaders were sent to Australia instead.
- Robert Owen set up a factory in New Lanark in Scotland that offered free schooling to workers' children, provided houses for workers near the factory and would not employ any child below the age of 10.
- Lord Shaftesbury forced the government to pass the Factory Acts which limited the hours that children and workers could work. In 1842 children and women were no longer allowed to work in mines.

**(b) Write an account of a factory or mine owner in Britain during the Industrial Revolution. Simply write an account using most of the facts from above and add the following facts:**

### Home Life

- The owners lived in large houses away from the slums of the workers.
- There were so many people looking for work that owners were able to offer very low wages to their workers. This meant that they could earn large profits.
- Servants would help clean, cook and serve in the large houses. Private tutors would teach the children and the children usually went on to university.
- Holidays were often spent in the countryside or by the seaside and they would be able to travel there by train.

## Question 5:

**(a) Read the following accounts by three fictional characters at the beginning of the Agricultural Revolution and answer the questions that follow:**

### THE FARM WORKER

*My name is Mr Andrews. I live in the village in a small one-roomed hut with my family: five girls and two boys. I don't own any land unfortunately so I can't grow any crops, but I do manage to use some of the common land available near the marsh so that I can grow some vegetables and potatoes. It's not much, but with the money that Mrs Andrews makes from selling the eggs from the geese she has on the village common, and the money I get from the squire and the big farmer, we manage to survive. Unfortunately the big farmer, Mr Ambrose doesn't always want workers - he says he only needs them sometimes so we're not always sure that the money will keep coming in!*

*It gets very cold in the winter but we keep each other warm and the children get as many sticks and pieces of timber as possible from the woods. There seems to be a lot of things to eat and keep ourselves warm with in the woods. If we didn't have the woods, the commons to let the goose feed and the marsh to grow things, we would starve.*

### THE SMALL FARMER

Hello there, my name is Mr Brown. My family has lived around here for the last four generations. My father and his father worked very hard and now we have 10 acres around the village. It's all divided up and I grow all my barley in one field and my wheat in another. The third strip I leave empty or fallow as it is called. What I grow isn't much but it brings in a little money so I can pay the rent. The rest of my possessions are mostly for ourselves or for selling at the market. I have a few sheep, geese and cattle on the village commons and they provide milk, eggs, wool and in the winter some meat. I don't have anywhere else to put them so they have to eat the grass out there with all the other animals. They are skinny wretches, but they do. Sure, what else can you do? I live here with Mrs Brown and the family. We have this nice two-roomed cottage that we live in, and what branches and timber we find in the woods keeps us warm and snug - sometimes we get mushrooms and berries in the woods too. I'd love to buy somewhere bigger, but I never have that much money left over after I've paid the rent to the landlord. We get by, and even in the winter we don't get too hungry. All in all, right now, as it is, we survive - just.

## The large landowner

*I am Mr Ambrose. I'm very important around here. I own a lot of land in this area. Actually I don't know how much, but I think it must be about 80 to 100 acres. The problem is I don't know as it is dotted all over the place. Some fields are barley, some wheat and the rest I just let sit and lay empty or fallow - it's an awful waste! It is a real inconvenience that I have to travel all the time from field to field, but that's the way it is I suppose. I get some of the labourers to work in the fields and they are so lazy. It seems to me there are so many of them doing the work - if only there was a machine that would do the work for me!*

*All my cattle are in the village commons. I leave them there, although I wish I had somewhere they could be put, as I don't like them around those disgusting labourers and their cattle because of all the diseases they carry. Nevertheless, although the cattle and sheep are all very skinny, there is nothing I can do. All the animals keep breeding with the other cattle! I sell a lot of the cattle to the market if I need to, but making money isn't really too difficult with all this land.*

*I have been hearing about all these new methods and new ways of doing things. I would love to try them, but it is so difficult with all the travelling and moving things around. I would love to have some land of my own to experiment with the new methods and to keep all my sheep and cattle together away from all the nasty unhealthy ones!*

**(i) Outline the changes that will occur to each of the characters:**

**(ii) Explain how enclosure helped to advance the Industrial Revolution.**

**(b) Examine the map of Ireland showing the fall in population in different parts of the country after the Famine 1845-1848**

**(i) What areas of Ireland suffered the greatest fall in population?**

**(ii) What <u>three</u> areas experienced a growth in population?**

**(iii) Why do you think those areas experienced a growth in population?**

**(iv) What relationship do you think there was between the dramatic fall in the number of Irish speakers and the fall in population across the country?**

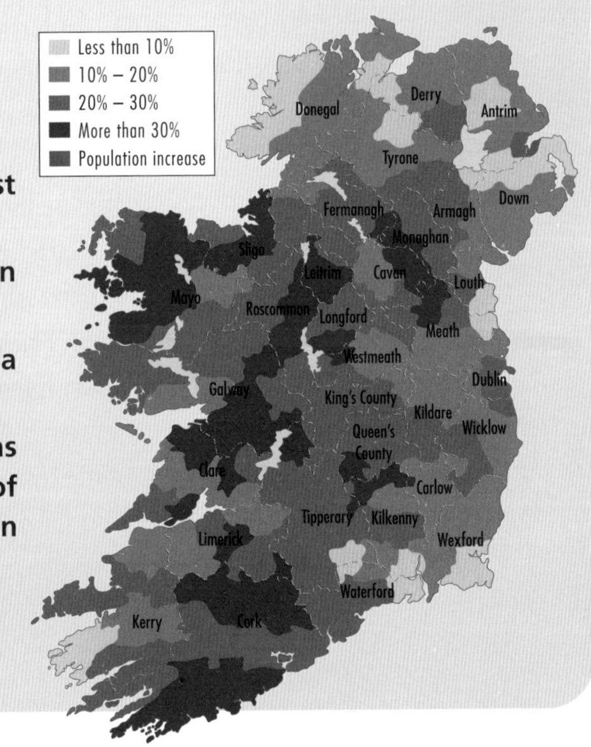

## (a) Picture A

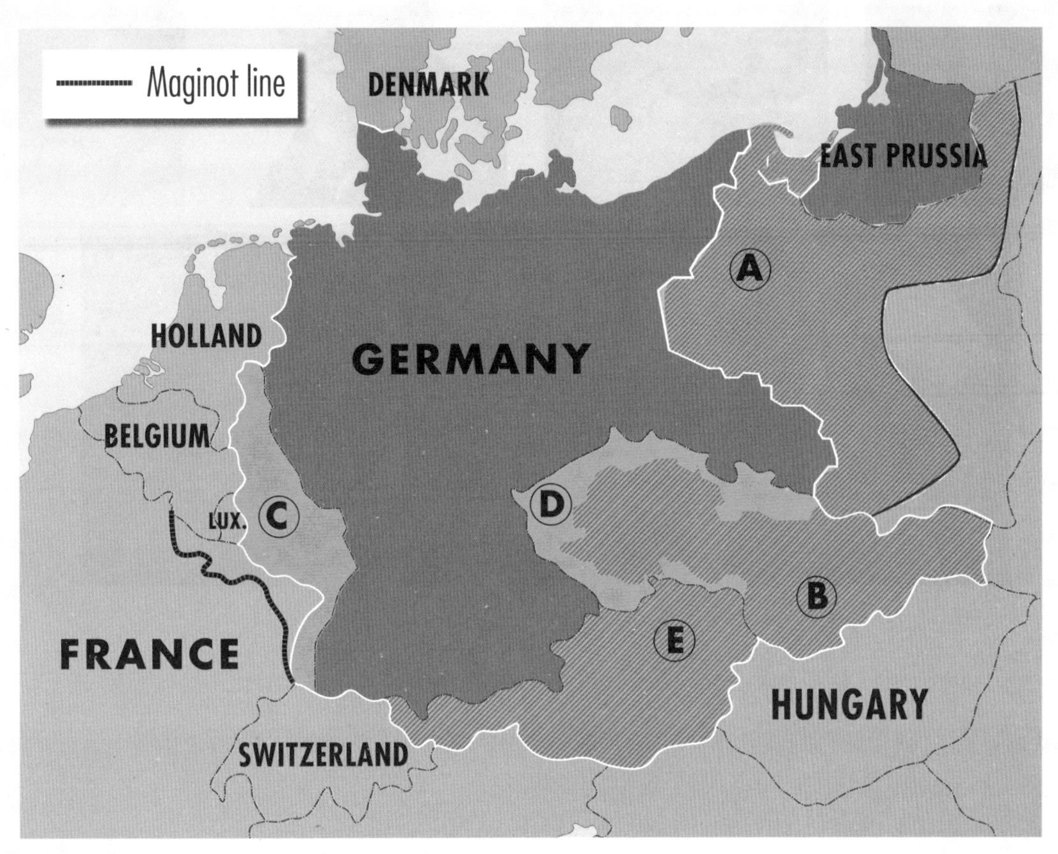


**Examine Picture A and then answer the following questions:**

(i) Name each of the labelled areas of German expansion (A, B, C, D and E) during the years leading up to World War II.

(ii) Put the areas in chronological (time) order of expansion.

(iii) What was the name given to the unification of Austria and Germany?

(iv) With whom did Germany sign an agreement before its invasion of Poland?

(v) What was the policy called that Chamberlain followed when he met Hitler in Munich in September 1938?

## (b) Picture B

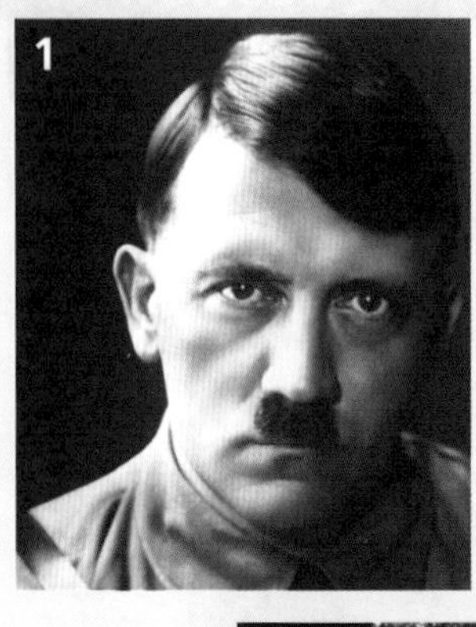

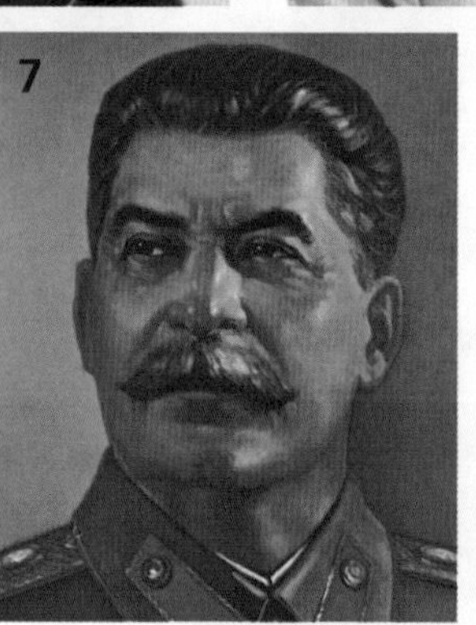


**Examine the pictures (1-7) and then answer the following questions:**

(i) Name each of the leaders in the pictures above.
(ii) State the countries in which they were leaders.
(iii) State the <u>three</u> leaders who were allied during World War II.
(iv) Choose <u>three</u> leaders from the pictures above and briefly outline their role in World War II.

## (b) Picture C

**Examine the cartoon entitled 'The Uneasy Alliance' and answer the questions that follow:**

(i) Name the two leaders in the cartoon.
(ii) What was the 'uneasy alliance' that the cartoon refers to?
(iii) Why does the artist believe it is an 'uneasy' alliance?
(iv) Give <u>two</u> reasons why this alliance was such a surprising one.

## Question 2: DOCUMENTS

Study Documents 1 and 2 below, and then answer the following questions.

### (a) Document 1

The extract below is by Richard Glazer. In it he describes arriving at Treblinka extermination camp.

We got out stepping on each other. We saw men wearing blue armbands. Some carried whips. We saw some SS men - Green uniforms, black uniforms. We were a mass, and the mass swept us along. It was irresistible. It had to move to another place. I saw the others undressing. And I heard: 'Get undressed - you're to be disinfected.'

As I waited already naked, I noticed the SS men separating out some people. These were told to get dressed. A passing SS man suddenly stopped in front of me, looked me over, and said, 'Yes, you too, quick, join the others, get dressed. You're going to work here, and if you're good, you can be a Kapo - a squad leader.' We were taken to a barracks. The whole place stank.

Piled about five feet high in a jumbled mess, were all the things people could conceivably have brought - clothes, suitcases, everything stacked in a solid mass. On top of it, jumping around like demons, people were making bundles and carrying them outside. It was turned over to one of these men. His armband said 'Squad Leader.'

He shouted and I understood that I was also to pick up clothing, bundle it and take it somewhere. As I worked I asked him, 'What's going on? Where are the ones who stripped?' And he replied, 'Dead all dead!'

(i) What was the SS uniform?
(ii) Why were the prisoners told to get undressed?
(iii) What was the reason Richard Glazer was told to get dressed again?
(iv) Who were the people who made the bundles of clothes?
(v) Where had the items in the barracks come from?
(vi) What had happened to the rest of the people who had arrived to Treblinka?
(vii) What was meant by the 'Final Solution'?

## (b) Document 2

The statement below was given by Neville Chamberlain as he stood outside 10 Downing Street in 1938. Read the statement and answer the questions that follow:

> We, the German Fuhrer and Chancellor, and the British Prime Minister, have had a further meeting today and are agreed in recognizing that the question of Anglo-German relations is of the first importance for our two countries and for Europe.
>
> We regard the agreement signed last night and the Anglo-German Naval Agreement as symbolic of the desire of our two peoples never to go to war with one another again.
>
> We are resolved that the method of consultation shall be the method adopted to deal with any other questions that may concern our two countries, and we are determined to continue our efforts to remove possible sources of difference, and thus to contribute to assure the peace of Europe.
>
> My good friends, for the second time in our history, a British Prime Minister has returned from Germany bringing peace with honour. I believe it is 'peace for our time'. Go home and get a nice quiet sleep.

(i) Name the German Führer and Chancellor.

(ii) What agreement is Chamberlain referring to in this speech?

(iii) How does Chamberlain hope to contribute 'to assure the peace of Europe'?

(iv) Where did the meeting between Chamberlain and the German Führer take place?

(v) What was decided at this meeting?

(vi) Did the agreement bring 'peace for our time'? Give reasons for your answer.

## Question 3:
## SHORT-ANSWER QUESTIONS

(a) Explain the following terms:

(i) Reparations
(ii) Communism
(iii) Fascism
(iv) March on Rome
(v) Acerbo Law
(vi) Intimidation
(vii) Propaganda
(viii) Indoctrination
(ix) Nazism
(x) Night of Broken Glass
(xi) Lebensraum
(xii) Gestapo
(xiii) Appeasement
(xiv) The Blitz
(xv) Kamikaze
(xvi) Holocaust

(b) Examine the pictures (1-5). Name each person and state their role within the Nazi party.

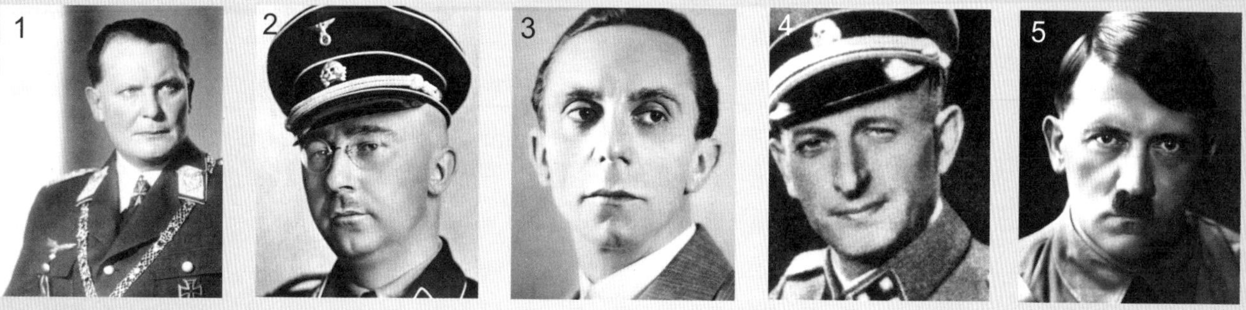

1 2 3 4 5

(c) Explain the term Blitzkrieg and how it operated.

(d) Fill in the gaps: Rewrite the following sentences and fill in the missing words:

(i) World War I, or the G_____ W____ as it was known, ended with a peace conference in P____. The peace treaty became known as the T_______ of V________ and was signed in 1919.

(ii) Germany had to agree to pay r________ to the victorious allies and accept that the war was caused by Germany's actions. This was known as the W____ G____ C______.

(iii) Tsar N_________ of Russia was overthrown and in October 1917 the B_______ Party led by V_______ L_____ took over the government of Russia.

(iv) When L_____ died, J____ S_______ took over as leader of the C______ Party in 1924 and began to industrialise the USSR.

(v) Benito M__________ founded the Italian F_______ Party and they gained power using a mixture of intimidation and p_____________.

(vi) The F_______ also i___________ young people through after-school clubs called *balilla*.

(vii) M________ and Hitler created an alliance called the R______-B_______ A_____.

(viii) The German Nazi party's full name was the N_________ S_________ G________ W________ P________.

(ix) The Nazi Sturm Abteilung (SA) were also known as the B___________ ___________.

(x) Hitler was imprisoned after the Munich Beer-Hall P_______ and while in prison wrote his book *M*______ *K*_______.

(xi) Hitler sent his troops into the demilitarised R________ in 1936 and unified with Austria under the *A*_________ in 1938.

(xii) The war broke out after Germany's invasion of P_________ in 1939.

(xiii) Germany was initially very successful but in 1942 they were defeated at S_________ in the USSR and at El A_______ in Africa.

(xiv) The day of the invasion of Europe from Britain in 19___ was known as D-Day or D_________ Day.

(xv) President T_________ of America agreed to drop two a______ bombs on the cities of H____________ and N_________ in Japan in 1945.

(xvi) It is thought that about six million Jews were killed during World War II by the Nazis in what is known as the H__________.

(e) Write a sentence explaining each of the following people's relevance during the first half of the twentieth century.

(i) Woodrow Wilson
(ii) Vladimir Lenin
(iii) Leon Trotsky
(iv) Josef Stalin
(v) Benito Mussolini
(vi) King Victor Emmanuel III
(vii) General Franco
(viii) Ernst Rohm
(ix) General Erwin Rommel
(x) General Montgomery
(xi) General Zhukov

(f) Name the country that launched the following operations and state the objective of each:

(i) Barbarossa
(ii) Sealion
(iii) Eagle
(iv) Overlord
(v) Uranus

(g) Link the following locations (1-6) with the correct events (a-f):

| Location | | Event |
|---|---|---|
| 1 Dunkirk | (a) | Defeat of German General Rommel by British General Montgomery in 1942. |
| 2 Stalingrad | (b) | The decisive naval battle of the war in the Pacific won by the Americans against the Japanese. |
| 3 El Alamein | (c) | Hawaiian naval base where the Japanese air force attacked the American navy. |
| 4 Midway | (d) | The area of Czechoslovakia containing ethnic Germans that Hitler wished to annex in 1938. |
| 5 Sudetenland | (e) | Perhaps the decisive battle between the Soviet army and the Wehrmacht, won by the Soviet army in 1942. |
| 6 Pearl Harbour | (f) | The port from which the Allied forces fled back to Britain in 1940. |

(h) Explain the following military terms:

(i) Wehrmacht
(ii) Luftwaffe
(iii) Spitfire
(iv) Stuka
(v) Messerschmitt
(vi) Panzer
(vii) U-Boat
(viii) Hurricane
(ix) RAF

## Question 4: PEOPLE IN HISTORY

**Write an account of a person living in London during the Blitz using the following guidelines or hints.**

HINTS:
* Outbreak of the war
* War comes close
* The Blitz
* The Battle of Britain

### The outbreak of the war

- British Prime Minister Neville Chamberlain tried to appease Hitler at the Munich Conference in 1938 but this proved unsuccessful.
- In 1939, Germany invaded Poland, so Britain declared war on Germany.
- The first six months of the war were very quiet and were known as the Phoney War because nothing happened.
- Londoners used this time to build up supplies and prepare for any invasion.
- Husbands, brothers and sons were sent to the army for training and women began to work in factories making ammunition and other essential supplies.
- Children were evacuated from cities and sent to live with people in the countryside.
- The government distributed gas masks and started to organise underground shelters.

### War comes close

- In April 1940, Germany invaded Denmark and later the Netherlands, Belgium and then France.
- Over 250,000 British Expeditionary Forces were sent to France to help but they were taken by surprise at the speed of Germany's Blitzkrieg.
- 350,000 British and French troops had to be evacuated from Dunkirk. Anyone who had a boat was asked to sail to Dunkirk and collect as many men as possible. 330,000 men were rescued.
- By 22 June 1940 Paris had surrendered to the Germans.

### The Blitz

- Hitler's plans to invade Britain were called Operation Eagle and Operation Sealion.
- He planned to defeat Britain in the air first and then launch a naval invasion called Operation Sealion.
- In August 1940 the German Luftwaffe began their bombing campaign on air bases, oil refineries and then London itself.
- Whenever the bombing started, air-raid sirens were played all across the cities. People were expected to find their way to underground shelters for safety.
- They would often have to sleep there until the bombing raids finished even if that was for weeks at a time.
- The raids lasted for 57 consecutive days and killed over 40,000 Londoners.

### The Battle of Britain

- Throughout the Blitz, the Royal Air Force's (RAF) Spitfire and Hurricane fighter-planes would attack the German fighter-planes called Messerschmitts and Stukas. These fights were known as 'dog-fights'.
- The RAF managed to shoot down many German bombers and therefore Hitler called off Operation Eagle. On 10 May 1941 the very last bombing raid of the Blitz took place and killed almost 1,500 people.

## Question 5:

(a) Write a paragraph on two of the following topics:
  (i) The war in the Pacific
  (ii) The Holocaust
  (iii) D-Day
  (iv) The March on Rome

(b) This poster asks 'Children, what do you know about your leader?' and is an example of Nazi propaganda. Examine the picture and answer the questions below:
  (i) Who is the 'leader' in the picture?
  (ii) Why did the Nazis want children to learn about their leader?
  (iii) What impression is the viewer expected to get from the poster about the man in the picture? Give reasons for your answer using the picture as evidence.
  (iv) Give an example of another method of propaganda used by German or Italian Fascists.
  (v) Explain how children were indoctrinated in Fascist Germany or Italy. Give two examples of indoctrination.

(c) On 13 February 1945, just over two months before the unconditional surrender of Germany and Hitler's suicide – with Germany defeated in all but name, Britain bombed the city of Dresden. 135,000 people were killed and 80% of the city was destroyed. Do you think that this action was justified or not? Give reasons for your answer.

# Chapter 12 IRELAND IN THE TWENTIETH CENTURY

## Question 1: PICTURES

## (a) Picture A

**Examine Picture A of an Irish leader of the Irish War of Independence 1919-1921 and answer the following questions:**

(i) Name the Irish leader in Picture A.

(ii) State one major contribution that this leader made to the War of Independence.

(iii) Outline the events of his death. Give at least <u>three</u> points in your answer.

(iv) Name one other Irish leader of the War of Independence.

(v) Explain briefly how the War of Independence contributed to the outbreak of the Irish Civil War, 1922-1923.

## (b) Picture B

**Examine Picture B – the map of Ulster showing the 1910 election results – and answer the following questions:**

(i) Name the political parties that won the seats in the following locations: **(a)** Mid Antrim **(b)** South Down **(c)** North Fermanagh **(d)** South Tyrone **(e)** South Monaghan

(ii) In which constituency did the Liberal party win a seat?

(iii) Explain the terms 'unionist' and 'nationalist'.

(iv) Name a unionist leader during the Home Rule Crisis, 1910-1914.

(v) What was meant by Home Rule?

(vi) Why do you think that most of the unionist seats are in the east of Ulster? Give reasons for your answer.

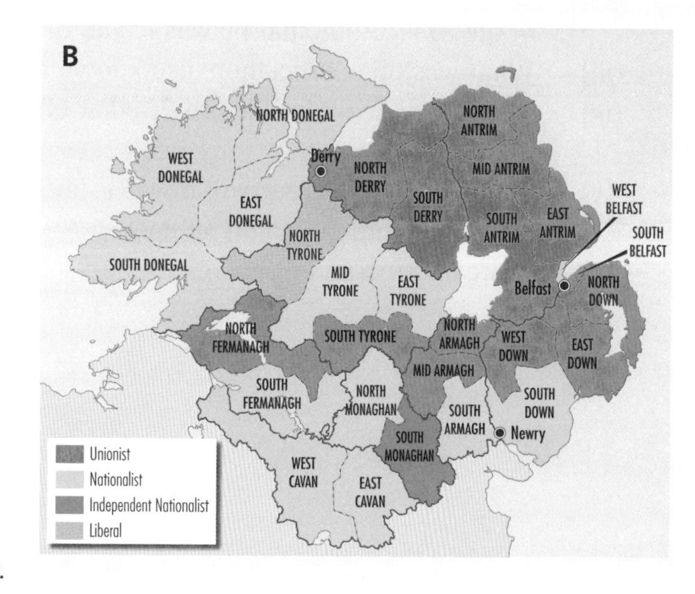

## (c) Picture C

**Examine Picture C and answer the following questions.**

(i) Name the Irish leader marked X at the centre of Picture C.

(ii) Until its name was changed to the National Guard in 1933, what was the official name of the Association that he was leader of?

(iii) What was this Association also known as?

(iv) Using evidence from Picture C, what other European political movement was this group similar to?

(v) Name the political party that was formed by the union of this Association, the Centre Party and Cumann na nGaedhael.

(vi) Write an account of the organisation set up in 1932.

## Question 2: DOCUMENTS

Study Documents **1, 2** and **3** below, and then answer the following questions.

### (a) Document 1

This is an extract from the Proclamation of the Irish Republic issued by the leaders of the 1916 Rising.

IRISHMEN AND IRISHWOMEN: In the name of God and of the dead generations from which she receives her old tradition of nationhood, Ireland, through us, summons her children to her flag and strikes for her freedom.

Having organised and trained her manhood through her secret revolutionary organisation, the Irish Republican Brotherhood, and through her open military organisations, the Irish Volunteers and the Irish Citizen Army, having patiently perfected her discipline . . . supported by her exiled children in America and by gallant allies in Europe, but relying in the first on her own strength, she strikes in full confidence of victory.

The Irish Republic is entitled to, and hereby claims, the allegiance of every Irishman and Irishwoman. The Republic guarantees religious and civil liberty, equal rights and equal opportunities to all its citizens, and declares its resolve to pursue the happiness and prosperity of the whole nation and all its parts, cherishing all of the children of the nation equally, and oblivious of the differences carefully fostered by an alien government, which have divided a minority from the majority in the past.

We place the cause of the Irish Republic under the protection of the Most High God, Whose blessing we invoke upon our arms, and we pray that no one who serves that cause will dishonour it by cowardice, inhumanity, or rapine.

(i) From whom does Ireland receive her 'old tradition of nationhood'?

(ii) Name the secret organisation that 'trained her manhood'.

(iii) Name one other organisation that is named as also training 'her manhood'.

(iv) What evidence is there to show that the Rising had support from outside Ireland?

(v) List three things that the Republic guarantees.

(vi) What had the 'alien government' done in the past?

(vii) What government is being referred to when the authors write about an 'alien government'?

(viii) What evidence is there to show that the authors of the Proclamation were religious?

(ix) What actions would dishonour the cause?

(x) Name two leaders of the 1916 Rising.

(xi) Name one of the main locations of the 1916 Rising.

## (b) Document 2

This is an extract from a speech by Professor Hayes of the National University during the Dáil debates on the Treaty on Wednesday 21 December 1921.

In judging this Treaty I take two standards, first the question of our honour, and the second question is whether under this Treaty we have the substance of freedom. Our representatives, the representatives of the historic Irish nation, negotiated in London for two months with the representatives of England and with the eyes of the world upon them. Now I submit, in spite of any legal quibbles, that fact in itself went a long way towards recognising the status of the independent national entity which we call the Irish Nation. [hear, hear]... We were told plainly and distinctly by our ambassadors in foreign parts that no nation in the world recognises an Irish Republic, and more recognition has been given to Ireland by England than has been given by any other nation in the world; and if we have the courage to grasp that and act in the light of that achievement we will be doing right [hear, hear]... This Treaty defines our relations with the British Commonwealth of Nations. It is not a concession, not a Home Rule Bill, but an international instrument, not granting us rights but acknowledging rights that have long been questioned and are now admitted in face of the world by England... I submit that in this Treaty we have the substance of freedom if we have the courage to take it; and when we are asked, 'Is this what has been fought for?' I say that if the words of the Treaty give you the right to say that England must get out of Ireland then that is what was fought for [hear, hear].

(i) What are the two standards on which the speaker will judge the Treaty?

(ii) For how long did the negotiations between the representatives of Ireland and those of England take place?

(iii) What evidence is there that no foreign countries have recognised Ireland's independence?

(iv) What form of freedom does this Treaty offer if the Irish people 'have the courage to take it'?

(v) What does the speaker believe was 'what has been fought for'?

(vi) List two of the negotiators on the Irish side of the Treaty negotiations.

(vii) Name the British Prime Minister who negotiated the Treaty.

(viii) Name an Irish leader of the Pro-Treaty side and one from the Anti-Treaty side.

(ix) Outline how the Treaty caused the Irish Civil War of 1922-1923.

(x) Give an account of two of the main events of the Irish Civil War.

## (c) Document 3

The following is an extract from a speech made by Jim Larkin, reported in the *Freeman's Journal,* October 1913.

'I have tried to kill sectarianism, whether in Catholics or Protestants. I am against bigotry or intolerance on either side. Those who want to divide the workers have resorted to the foulest methods. I have not read the evening papers, but I am informed vile things are stated in them. They have lit a fire in Ireland they will never put out. There will be a cry raised in England, Scotland, and Wales which will not be quietened for some time.'

'For years and years I have done the work I was born for. I have proved there were 21,000 families living five in a room in Dublin . . . I have raised the morals and sobriety of the people. Even Murphy says Larkin has done good, but "hands off the trams". I have taken no man's honour or no woman's honour. I never stood in a public house bar and alcoholic drink never touched my lips. I am careful about my conduct because I know this cause requires clean men.'

(i) What did Larkin claim to have proved?

(ii) What improvements in people's lives does he claim to have made?

(iii) Why has he 'never stood in a public house bar and alcoholic drink never touched' his lips?

(iv) Who is the Murphy mentioned in the extract and why did he say, 'hands off the trams'?

(v) Write an account of the 1913 Lockout.

(vi) Why do you think there were people who wanted 'to divide the workers' using the 'foulest methods'?

## Question 3: SHORT-ANSWER QUESTIONS

### Home Rule Crisis and 1916 Rising

(a) Explain the aims of the following organisations:

(i) The GAA (ii) The Gaelic League (iii) The Abbey Theatre (iv) Irish Citizen Army

(b) Match each leader in Column A with the corresponding item in Column B.

| Column A | Column B |
|---|---|
| 1 Douglas Hyde | (a) The Abbey Theatre |
| 2 Edward Carson | (b) ITGWU |
| 3 Michael Cusack | (c) The Irish Parliamentary Party |
| 4 Lady Gregory | (d) The Solemn League and Covenant |
| 5 James Connolly | (e) Dublin United Tramways Company |
| 6 John Redmond | (f) Irish Citizen Army |
| 7 Eoin MacNeill | (g) National Volunteers |
| 8 Jim Larkin | (h) British Prime Minister |
| 9 William Martin Murphy | (i) Irish National Volunteers |
| 10 Arthur Griffith | (j) The GAA |
| 11 Herbert Asquith | (k) Sinn Féin |

(c) Name the political leaders from the period 1900-1920 in the pictures (A-F) below:

A

B

C

D

E

F

(d) Explain the following terms:

(i) Nationalist
(ii) Unionist
(iii) Partition
(iv) Home Rule
(v) Anglicisation
(vi) Solemn League and Covenant
(vii) Lockout
(viii) Anglo-Irish Literary Revival
(ix) Conscription
(x) Blood sacrifice

(e) What was meant by 'Ulster Day' in 1912?

(f) Where did the UVF land their guns and ammunition in 1914?

(g) What was the Curragh Mutiny?

(h) Who set up Sinn Féin?

(i) Explain the importance of the 'Castle Document' in the success or failure of the 1916 Rising.

(j) Give two reasons for the growth in Sinn Féin's popularity after 1916.

(k) Fill in the gaps: rewrite the following sentences and fill in the missing words.

(i) N____________ in Ireland wanted to achieve some form of i____________ from Britain.

(ii) U____________ in Ireland feared that any form of H____________ R____________ would result in religious domination by C__________. They worried that 'H____________ R____________ would mean R____________ Rule'.

(iii) The GAA was set up in 18____________ by Michael C____________ and Maurice D____________ . They hoped to promote G____________ games such as h____________ , Gaelic f____________ and handball.

(iv) The G____________ L____________ was set up by Douglas H____________ and E____________ MacN____________ in 1893. They hoped to halt the decline of the Irish language.

(v) WB Y____________ and Lady G____________ set up the____________ Theatre in 19____________ to promote Irish writers.

(vi) Jim L________ established the I____________ T____________ and G____________ W____________ U____________ . This was opposed by William M____________ M____________ owner of the Dublin U____________ T____________ Company and resulted in the 1913 L____________ of workers.

(vii) James C____________ set up the Irish L____________ Party in 1912 and then organised the Irish C____________ Army in 1913.

(viii) Ulster U____________ opposed H____________ Rule and in September 1912 400,000 signed the Solemn L____________ and C____________ . This stated that they would never accept H____________ R____________ .

(ix) U______________ set up the U______________ V______________ F______________ which was prepared to resist H______________ R______________ with force if necessary.

(x) In 1915, a five-man IRB M______________ C______________ was set up to prepare for a rebellion to take place on E______ Sunday 19______________ .

(xi) Roger C______________ and his ship, the *A*______________ , were captured by the British navy as he returned with ammunition and guns from Germany.

(xii) Arthur G______________ set up the political party called S______________ F______________ in 1905.

## War of Independence and Civil War

(a) From where did de Valera escape in 1919?

(b) Who was in charge of the Irish Republican Army?

(c) What event is thought to have marked the beginning of the Irish War of Independence?

(d) Explain the following terms:

(i) Flying columns
(ii) Black and Tans
(iii) Auxiliaries
(iv) Guerrilla warfare
(v) Bloody Sunday 1920
(vi) The Squad
(vii) Commonwealth
(viii) Regulars and Irregulars

(e) Place the following people in the correct category, i.e. Pro-Treaty or Anti-Treaty.

(i) Michael Collins
(ii) Eamon de Valera
(iii) Cathal Brugha
(iv) Arthur Griffith
(v) Harry Boland
(vi) Kevin O'Higgins
(vii) Rory O'Connor

(f) What is meant by 'Treaty Ports'? Name them.

(g) What was the name given to the newly independent Ireland created by the Treaty?

(h) What is the Oath of Allegiance and why did some Irish leaders dislike taking it?

(i) Give one result of the Irish Civil War.

(j) Fill in the gaps: rewrite the following sentences and fill in the missing words.

(i) S_____________ F_____________ won 73 seats at the 1918 election and decided to set up an Irish government instead of going to W_____________ .

(ii) On 21 January they established D_____________ É_____________ and elected Cathal B_____________ president as de V_______ was still in prison. The Irish V_________ became known as the I_____________ R_____________ A_____________ and was led by Michael C_____________ .

(iii) C_____________ organised the IRA by creating groups of g_____________ fighters known as f_____________ c_____________ .

(iv) The British government brought in ex-soldiers from World War I to fight against the IRA. These British soldiers were known as B_____________ and T_____________ as they wore both khaki and the RIC uniforms.

(v) The S_____________ F_____________ Mayor of Cork, T_____________ MacS_____________ died after 73 days of hunger strike when he was arrested and imprisoned by the British.

(vi) On Sunday 21 November 1920, Collins' S_____________ killed 11 British secret-service men. In retaliation, the B_____________ and T_____________ shot 12 spectators at a football match at Croke Park. The day became known as B_____________ S_____________ .

(vii) In December 1920, much of C_____________ city centre was burnt down by the B_____________ and T_____________ .

(viii) The T_____________ was signed on 6 December 1921. It created the Irish F_____________ S_____________ . It remained within the British C_____________ and all TDs would have to swear an O_____________ of A_____________ to the British king.

(ix) A B_____________ C_____________ was to be set up to decide the border between N_____________ Ireland and the Irish F_____________ S_____________ .

(x) Britain kept control over the Treaty ports: L_____________ S_____________ , Q_____________ (modern day C_____________ ) and B_____________ .

(xi) The Irish C_____________ War began in June 1922 when Collins ordered the bombardment of the F_____________ C_____________ which had been occupied by Rory O_____________ and the anti-Treaty Irregulars.

(xii) Michael C_____________ was killed at B_____________ na mB_____________ , County Cork in August 1922 and de Valera agreed to a c_____________ in May 1923.

## Independent Ireland (1922-1945)

(a) Name the people associated with the early years of Ireland's independence in the pictures (A-D) below:

(b) What was the Boundary Commission?

(c) Explain the following terms:

| | | |
|---|---|---|
| (i) The ACC | (iii) The Emergency | (v) Rationing |
| (ii) The Blueshirts | (iv) the LDF | (vi) Neutrality |

(d) What was the Statute of Westminster and how did it contribute to the destruction of the Treaty?

(e) Match the political leaders in Column A with the appropriate party in Column B:

| **Column A** | **Column B** |
|---|---|
| 1 Seán Lemass | (a) Fine Gael |
| 2 William T. Cosgrave | (b) Fianna Fáil |
| 3 Eoin O'Duffy | (c) Cumann na nGaedhael |
| 4 Kevin O'Higgins | |
| 5 Eamon de Valera | |

(f) List two achievements of the Cumann na nGaedhael government of 1922-1932.

(g) List two reasons for the success of the Fianna Fáil party in the 1932 election.

(h) Explain what new laws were introduced with the following Acts:

(a) The Public Safety Acts of 1923 and 1924

(b) The Public Safety (Emergency powers) Act, 1926

(c) The Electoral Amendment Act, 1927

(d) The Emergency Powers Act, 1939

(i) Give one positive consequence and one negative consequence of The Emergency on Ireland.

(j) Fill in the gaps: rewrite the following sentences and fill in the missing words.

(i) C______________ na nG______________ was led by William T C______________ . They created a new constitution and established the O______________ (Houses of Parliament) named the D______________ and the S______________ .

(ii) A new police force called An G______________ S______________ was set up by the Minister of Justice, Kevin O'______________ .

(iii) In March 1924, some members of the army opposed the idea of reducing its size and m________.

(iv) Kevin O'______________ was assassinated in July 1927. This resulted in further laws controlling illegal organisations called the P______________ S______________ Act.

(v) F______________ F______________ was created by de V______________ and other S______________ F______________ members in 1926. F______________ F______________ set up a newspaper called *The I______________ P______________* in 1931.

(vi) De Valera used the S______________ of W__________ to dismantle the Treaty. By 1937 he had produced a new constitution called B______________ na hÉ______________ .

(vii) The A______ C________ A______________ was also known as the Blueshirts and was led by Eoin O'______________ In 1933, he changed the name of the ACA to the N______________ G______________ . Later this organisation would merge with other parties to form F______________ G______________ .

(viii) The E______________ W______________ of 1932-1938 was caused by the Irish government's refusal to pay land a______________ to Britain. It was finally settled with the A_____-Irish Agreement, 1938.

(ix) Ireland chose to remain n______________ during World War II. This period was known as The E______________ .

(x) There were shortages of food and raw materials so Seán L______________ , Minister of Supplies, introduced r______________ to ensure everyone got an equal share of goods like tea, flour and sugar.

## Question 4:
## PEOPLE IN HISTORY

**Write an account of a unionist living in Ulster during the Home Rule Crisis of 1912-1914 using the following guidelines or hints.**

HINTS:

* Family background
* Political Situation
* Political Parties in Ulster
* Methods of opposition

### Political Situation

➪ I am a Protestant linen merchant from Belfast. I have lived in Ireland all my life and my family have been here for centuries. I have a large house on the outskirts of the city.

➪ All of the island of Ireland is still part of the United Kingdom. Most of the island is made up of Catholics except in the eastern half of Ulster.

➪ Ulster industries have done well over the last number of decades: linen manufacturing, shipbuilding and rope-making have provided good employment.

➪ Some of the Catholics in the south of Ireland want Home Rule. This would give Dublin control over all of Ireland. We Protestants in Ulster do not want this for two reasons:

**(i)** If Dublin had control over trade, they might be more interested in agriculture and would not care about the industries in Ulster. The trade between Ulster and Britain may be harmed due to higher tariffs on exports to mainland Britain.

**(ii)** Furthermore, if there was an Irish Parliament in Dublin, it would be dominated by Catholics from the rest of Ireland, while at the moment, the Catholics in Ireland are a small minority among the Protestants in the United Kingdom. If Home Rule was passed, it might mean Rome Rule as the Irish Parliament would do as the Pope in Rome tells them to do! In fact, it is a matter of religious preservation.

### Political Parties in Ulster

➪ I am a member of the Unionist Party in the British Parliament in Westminster, London. The party is led by Edward Carson. They support the Conservative Party in parliament. One of the Ulster Unionist Party members, James Craig, organises rallies to show the unionist dislike for the idea of Home Rule and our loyalty to the Union of Britain and Ireland.

➪ I am also a member of the Orange Order. This is an organisation that only permits Protestants to join and is prepared to use whatever means are necessary to protect the Protestant way of life.

➪ Most of the Catholics in Ireland are nationalists. This means they want some form of independence from Britain. The Irish Parliamentary Party, led by John Redmond, hopes to get Home Rule passed soon.

## Methods of opposition

- Since the 1910 election, the IPP have had the balance of power. The Liberal Party in Britain led by Herbert Asquith passed the Home Rule Bill in 1912 and it was set to become law in 1914.
- The Ulster unionists were strongly against this and so Carson organised large demonstrations across Ulster. In September 1912, over 400,000 signed the Solemn League and Covenant stating that unionists would never accept Home Rule.
- To make sure that the British government understood how serious we were, James Craig encouraged unionists to set up the Ulster Volunteer Force. This is a military organisation prepared to use force to resist Home Rule.
- In 1914, almost 100,000 people became members of the UVF. We managed to smuggle almost 25,000 rifles and millions of rounds of ammunition into Larne in County Antrim.
- I am very sure we will be successful as the leader of the British Conservative Party has supported us too, even though the Irish nationalists have set up their own Volunteers called the Irish National Volunteers.

## Question 5:

**(i)** Write an account on three of the following:
- **(a)** The Home Rule Crisis, 1912-1914
- **(b)** Outline the main arguments for and against the Treaty.
- **(c)** The Emergency in Ireland
- **(d)** Cumann na nGaedhael in government, 1922-1932

**(ii)** Answer all the questions below:
- **(a)** Why did the Irish government pay £10 million to the British government under the terms of the Anglo-Irish Agreement of 1938?
- **(b)** Explain the importance of the Anglo-Irish Agreement, 1938.
- **(c)** Write an account of the Economic War of 1932-1938.

**(iii)** Answer both questions below:
- **(a)** Write an account of the roles played during the War of Independence and the Civil War by both Eamon de Valera and Michael Collins.
- **(b)** Which of the two leaders do you prefer? Give reasons for your answer.

## (a) Picture A

**Examine Picture A (a cartoon from 1948) and answer the following questions:**

(i) Which three countries' flags are shown in Picture A?
(ii) What city is being encircled?
(iii) Who or what is the bear supposed to represent? Give a reason for your answer.
(iv) What event is this image referring to?
(v) Name two leaders of any of the countries referred to in the picture during this event in 1948.

## (b) Picture B

**Examine Picture B which relates to the Cuban Missile Crisis and answer the following questions:**

(i) Name the two people in Picture B.
(ii) State which countries each of the leaders is from.
(iii) List two ways that the leaders in the picture helped to improve relations between their countries after the crisis had passed.
(iv) Outline the main events of the crisis. Give five points.

## (c) Picture C

**Examine Picture C (a graph showing the support in Ireland for the EU [EEC] since Ireland's accession in 1973) and answer the following questions:**

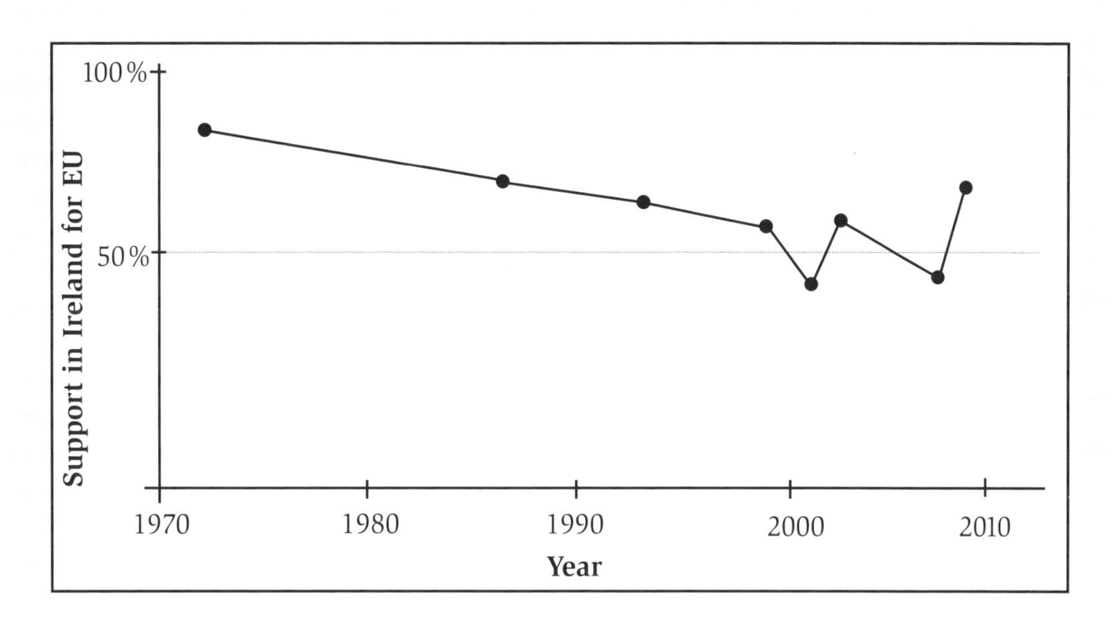


| Referendum | Year | % voted Yes | Result |
|---|---|---|---|
| Ireland's Accession to EEC | 1973: | 83.1% | Accepted |
| Single European Act | 1987: | 69.92% | Accepted |
| Maastricht Treaty | 1993: | 69.05% | Accepted |
| Amsterdam Treaty | 1999: | 61.74% | Accepted |
| EU Nice Treaty | 2001: | 46.13 % | Rejected |
| EU Nice Treaty II | 2002: | 62.89% | Accepted |
| EU Lisbon Treaty | 2008: | 46.6% | Rejected |
| EU Lisbon Treaty II | 2009: | 67.13% | Accepted |

(i) From your reading of the above data do you think that support for European integration in Ireland has increased or decreased since 1973?

(ii) Which referendum showed the highest support for European cooperation?

(iii) Which referendum had the least number of voters supporting further European cooperation?

(iv) Give two reasons why Ireland joined the EEC in 1973.

(v) Give one benefit and one criticism of the EU and its institutions.

## Question 2: DOCUMENTS

Study Documents **1** and **2** below, and then answer the following questions.

### (a) Document 1

This is an extract describing the Russian invasion of Hungary in 1956, taken from a newspaper article by journalist Noel Barber published in *The Daily Mail* on 27 October 1956.

'It took me three hours to drive from the border to the outskirts of Buda, the hilly part of Budapest. Twice on the way I was stopped by Soviet troops. But each time I persuaded them to let me through. I made for the Chain Bridge that spans the Danube. In front of the bridge stood a barricade of burned out tramcars, a bus, old cars, and uprooted tramlines. It was at least the 50th barricade of its kind I had seen since I entered the city. As I drove towards it, lights full on and the Chain Bridge on my left, heavy Bring (shots) started from the centre of the bridge. Machine-gun bullets whistled past the car. Then, when some heavier stuff began falling, I switched off the lights, jumped out and crawled round to the side.

'It was foggy. For ten minutes the firing, in a desultory fashion, went on. Then I heard a whispered voice – a woman's. She spoke first in German, crawled round to where I was crouching, then in halting English told me to get back in my car. She herself, walking, crouched by the car, guided me into a side street. Then, together, we darted back to the road-block.

'I found nine boys there, their average age about 18. Three wore Hungarian uniform, but with the hated Red Star torn off. Others wore red, green, and white armbands, the national colours of Hungary. All had sub-machine guns. Their pockets were filled with ammunition. The girl, whose name I discovered was Paula, had a gun too.

'Half-way across the bridge I could see the dim outlines of two Soviet tanks. For an hour they fired at us. But never a direct hit – a shell smashed straight through the bus. One of the boys was killed instantly. I tried to help a second boy who was hurt, but he died five minutes later. The shelling went on. We crouched under cover and only splinters hit us. The rebels kept up machine-gun fire all the time. Paula was wounded in the arm, but not seriously. I helped her dress it with one of my handkerchiefs.

"Now you see what we are fighting against", said Paula. She was wearing slacks, bright blue shoes, and a green overcoat.

"We will never give in – never", she said.

"Never until the Russians are out of Hungary and the AVH (she pronounced it Avo) (the Hungarian secret police) is dissolved".'

(i) Name the bridge that 'spans the Danube'.

(ii) Describe the barricade that was placed in front of the bridge.

(iii) Why do you think the author got out of the car he was travelling in? Use evidence from the document to support your answer.

(iv) What was the average age of the boys who he met?

(v) Why, do you think, had the boys torn 'the hated Red Star' off their uniforms?

(vi) What are the national colours of Hungary?

(vii) What did the 'rebels' hope to achieve? Give reasons for your answer using evidence from the document.

(viii) Name one other example where a superpower invaded another country.

## (b) Document 2

(2a) The following is an extract from Nikita Khrushchev's autobiography in which he discusses the Cuban Missile Crisis in 1962.

*The United States had already surrounded the Soviet Union with its own bomber bases and missiles. We knew that American missiles were aimed against us in Turkey and Italy, to say nothing of West Germany. It was during my visit to Bulgaria that I had the idea of installing missiles with nuclear warheads in Cuba without letting the United States find out they were there until it was too late to do anything about them. Everyone agreed that America would not leave Cuba alone unless we did something. We had an obligation to do everything in our power to protect Cuba's existence as a Socialist country and as a working example to the other countries in Latin America . . . The Americans had surrounded our country with military bases and threatened us with nuclear weapons and now they would learn just what it feels like to have enemy missiles pointing at you; we'd be doing nothing more than giving them a little of their own medicine.*

(2b) The following is a speech made by US President John F Kennedy on radio and television on 22 October 1962 to the American public.

*Good evening, my fellow citizens. This Government, as promised, has maintained the closest surveillance of the Soviet military build-up on the island of Cuba. Within the past week, unmistakable evidence has established the fact that a series of offensive missile sites is now in preparation on that imprisoned island. The purpose of these bases can be none other than to provide a nuclear strike capability against the Western Hemisphere . . . To halt this offensive build up, a strict quarantine on all offensive military equipment under shipment to Cuba is being initiated. All ships of any kind bound for Cuba from whatever nation or port will, if found to contain cargoes of offensive weapons, be turned back . . . We are not at this time, however, denying the necessities of life as the Soviets attempted to do in their Berlin blockade of 1948.*

(i) Where had the Americans placed missiles aimed at the USSR?

(ii) Why did Khrushchev believe it was necessary to protect Cuba?

(iii) What reasons did Cuba have for fearing further American aggression against the island?

(iv) What does Khrushchev mean when he states, 'we'd be doing nothing more than giving them a little of their own medicine'?

(v) What 'unmistakable evidence' had Kennedy established 'within the past week'?

(vi) What did Kennedy believe was the purpose of the bases?

(vii) List the measures Kennedy introduced to 'halt this offensive build-up'.

(viii) Why did Kennedy feel that what he was doing was not similar to events in Berlin in 1948?

(ix) Outline the compromise made between the USSR and the USA that ended the missile crisis.

## Question 3:
## SHORT-ANSWER QUESTIONS

### The Rise of the Superpowers

(a) Examine the pictures (A-H) below and state the names of each of the people involved in International Relations between 1945 and 2000.

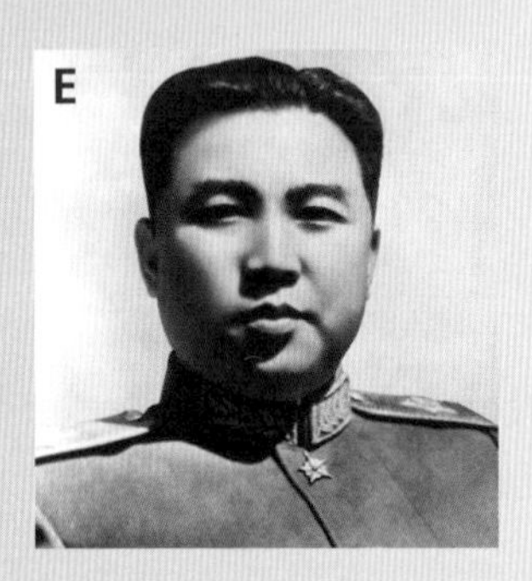

(b) Explain the following terms:

(i) Ideology
(ii) Cold War
(iii) Superpower
(iv) Iron curtain
(v) Perestroika
(vi) Glasnost
(vii) Puppet-state
(viii) Marshall Aid

(c) Match the countries in Column A with the correct terms in Column B.

| Column A | Column B |
|---|---|
| 1 USA | (a) Democracy |
| 2 USSR | (b) Communism |
| | (c) Capitalism |
| | (d) One party government |

(d) Explain the differences between capitalism and communism.

(e) Why did the USSR wish to create a 'buffer zone' around its borders after World War II?

(f) Outline the Truman Doctrine and give one example of it being put into operation.

(g) This map shows Berlin after it had been divided into four sectors.
  (i) List the four countries placed in charge of each of the sectors.
  (ii) Which country was in charge of the sector in the east of the city?

(h) What was Operation Vittles?

(i) What is the full name of NATO and why was it set up?

(j) Which two countries were separated by the 38th Parallel?

(k) Name the five permanent members of the UN Security Council.

(l) Give one result of the Korean War.

(m) Apart from Korea, Berlin and Cuba, list two other areas of conflict that involved either the USSR or the USA.

(n) Match the leaders in Column A with the appropriate term or event in Column B:

| **Column A** | **Column B** |
|---|---|
| 1 Harry Truman | (a) Glasnost |
| 2 Mikhail Gorbachev | (b) Cuban Missile Crisis |
| 3 Nikita Khrushchev | (c) Korean War |
| 4 General MacArthur | (d) Policy of containment |

(o) Fill in the gaps: rewrite the following sentences and fill in the missing words:

(i) The different views on how society works are called i______________ . This led to conflict between the USA and the USSR in what became known as the C______________ War.

(ii) The USSR wanted to have a buffer zone between it and Germany. The E______________ European countries became 'p______________ -states' of the USSR. Winston C______________ described the divide between east and west as an 'I______________ C______________ '.

(iii) American President Harry T______________ decided to try and stop the spread of communism through a policy of c______________ . This was called the Truman D______________ .

(iv) M______________ Aid was offered by the USA to all countries in Europe to rebuild the continent.

(v) Germany was divided into four sectors: B______________ , F______________ , A______________ and S______________ . Furthermore, Berlin was also divided up into four sectors with the S______________ sector in the e______________ . When a new German currency called the D______________ was introduced in the western sectors, the USSR refused to allow it be used in B______________ and therefore blockaded the city.

(vi) The Western Allies decided to fly supplies into west B_______________ in Operation V_______________ .

(vii) In 1961, a wall was built that divided the city of B_______________ into east and west.

(viii) The UN intervened in the K_______________ War on the side of South K_______________ to halt the advance of communist North K_______________ .

(ix) The C_______________ government sent troops to help North K_______________ and they pushed the UN troops south. Eventually both sides came to a stalemate at the _____________ th Parallel.

(x) After S_____________ 's death in 19_______________ both sides decided to sign an _______________ (ceasefire).

(xi) In 1962, the USSR offered to build missiles in C_____________ to ensure that the Americans would not try to invade C_______________ again like it had in 1961 at the B_______________ of P_______________ .

(xii) The American President John F. K_______________ announced that he would not allow missiles to be located in C_______________ and placed a naval b_______________ around the island.

(xiii) Eventually a compromise was found so that a full-scale n_______________ war was avoided. In 1963, a T_______________ B_______________ T_______________ was signed between the two countries that banned any testing of nuclear weapons.

(xiv) Following reforms by Mikhail G_______________ known as p_______________ and g_______________ the borders between east and western Europe opened and in 1989 even the B_______________ Wall was torn down.

## European Cooperation

(a) Explain the following terms:

| | | | |
|---|---|---|---|
| (i) OEEC | (iii) Common Market | (v) EURATOM | (vii) EFTA |
| (ii) ECSC | (iv) CAP | (vi) EEC | (viii) CFSP |

(b) Match the institutions in Column A with the correct functions they perform within the EU in Column B:

| **Column A** | **Column B** |
|---|---|
| 1 EU Commission | (a) Consists of national government ministers who are responsible for that particular area, e.g. agriculture |
| 2 Council of Ministers | (b) Ensures member states obey the laws made by the EU. |
| 3 European Parliament | (c) Made up of politicians appointed by the government of each member state. Can propose new laws. |
| 4 European Court of Justice | (d) Checks that all money that the EU receives is spent legally and correctly. |
| 5 European Court of Auditors | (e) Directly elected representatives of the member states depending on the size of its population. Can propose new laws. |

(c) What was the Benelux Union?

(d) List the six original members of the EEC.

(e) Explain what the Treaty of Rome established.

(f) Fill in the gaps: rewrite the following sentences and fill in the missing words.

(i) After World War II, E__________ leaders looked for ways to avoid another conflict. They thought that greater c__________ between countries would reduce the possibility of conflict.

(ii) To help distribute the money from the M__________ P__________, the O__________ for E__________ E__________ C__________ was set up.

(iii) Robert S__________ and Jean M__________ proposed that F__________ and G__________ should cooperate in the production of coal and steel.

(iv) In 1952, the E__________ C__________ and S__________ C__________ was set up.

(v) The T__________ of R__________ established the E__________ E__________ C__________ which abolished all custom duties, created a c__________ market and created the C__________ A__________ P__________ which offered farmers a guaranteed price for their produce.

(vi) In 1973, Ireland, the UK and D__________ joined the EEC.

(vii) The headquarters of the EEC is located in B__________ .

(viii) The European S__________ F__________ gives money to the poorer parts of the EEC to improve economic and social conditions.

(ix) The M__________ Treaty of 1992 renamed the European Community as the European U__________ and a new currency called the E__________ was introduced.

## Question 4:
## PEOPLE IN HISTORY

**Write an account of a person living in Berlin during the Blockade of 1948-1949 using the following hints:**

HINTS:

* The political situation after World War II
* The blockade by the Soviets
* The airlift by the Allies
* The results of the ending of the blockade

### The political situation after World War II

- Germany was divided into four sectors: British in the north west, Soviet in the east, American in the south and French along its border with Germany. Even though Berlin was in the Soviet sector, it was the capital of Germany, and therefore it was also divided into four sectors, just like the country – with the Soviets taking the east. This meant that West Berlin was totally surrounded by Soviet-controlled land.
- All of Germany was ruined. Disease and starvation were widespread across the country and millions died in the years after the end of the war. Although at the beginning, the Western Allies wanted to see Germany punished and made to pay for the war, they soon realised that they needed to help it to recover economically. Money from the Marshall Plan was used to rebuild the social and economic conditions in western Germany and in west Berlin.

### The blockade by the Soviets

- In an attempt to help Germany recover, a new currency called the Deutschmark was introduced in the western sectors. The Soviet government still did not want Germany to recover and therefore did not want the new currency to be used in Berlin.
- All roads and railways into Berlin were blocked by the Soviets. The USSR hoped that this would block the Western powers and that they would give up their sectors of Berlin. This frightened many of those living in the western sectors of Berlin who feared the Soviet government.

### The Airlift by the Allies

- The Western Allies decided that they would not give in to Soviet aggression and decided to fly supplies into Berlin by air. This was called Operation Vittles. Between June 1948 and May 1949, 270,000 flights delivered over 2 million tonnes of food, clothing and fuel into Berlin.
- There was even one pilot who dropped sweets and chocolate for the children from his aircraft.

### The results of the ending of the blockade

- In May 1949, the Soviets allowed the Western Allies to transport goods by land. Many people decided to leave East Germany and escape to the western sectors. To stop this, the East German government closed the border.
- When east Berliners tried to escape to west Berlin and from there go to the west, a wall was built. By 1961, the Berlin Wall divided the two sides of Berlin.

## Question 5:

**(i)** Write an account on two of the following topics:
- **(a)** The Cuban Missile Crisis, 1962
- **(b)** The Korean War, 1950-1953
- **(c)** The Berlin Blockade, 1948-1949

**(ii)** **(a** Explain why the Cold War developed between the USSR and the USA in the years immediately after World War II.
- **(b)** Outline the events that led to the collapse of communism in Eastern Europe.

**(iii)** **(a)** Name two politicians associated with the movement towards European unity in the years after World War II.
- **(b)** Outline the major moves towards European integration during the years up to the establishment of the EEC in 1957.
- **(c)** Write an account on two of the following pieces of European cooperation:
  - **1** The Single European Act, 1987
  - **2** The Maastricht Treaty, 1993
  - **3** The Amsterdam Treaty, 1999

Chapter 14

# IRELAND SINCE 1948

Question I: PICTURES

## (a) Picture A

**Examine the map below showing the increase in new TV licences in Ireland between 1965 and 1987 and then answer the following questions.**

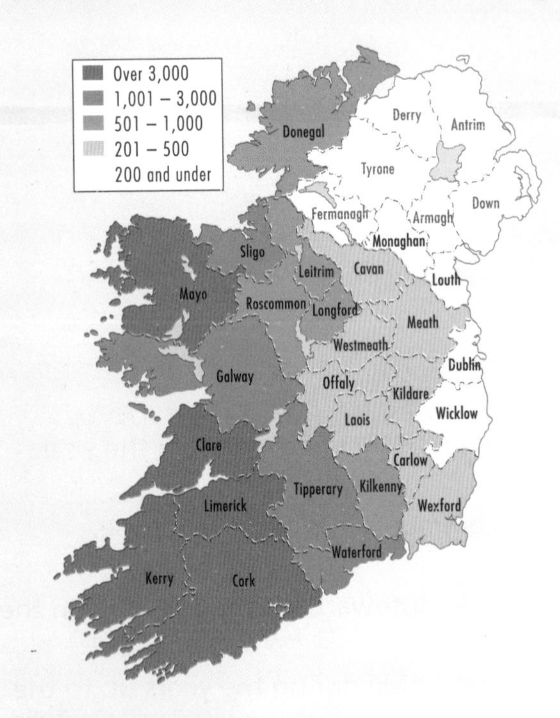


(i) Approximately how many new licences were issued during this time in the following counties:
   (a) Mayo
   (b) Leitrim
   (c) Louth

(ii) In which area of Ireland was the largest growth in new licences?

(iii) Why do you think the largest growth took place in this area?

(iv) What event in 1961 helped spread the influence of televisions in Ireland?

(v) How did televisions influence the Irish population's opinions during the 1960s and 1970s?

(vi) Name another event that took place between 1957 and 1973 in Ireland and how it influenced the Irish population.

## (b) Picture B

**Examine Pictures A-E (five photos of Taoisigh of Ireland) and answer the following questions:**

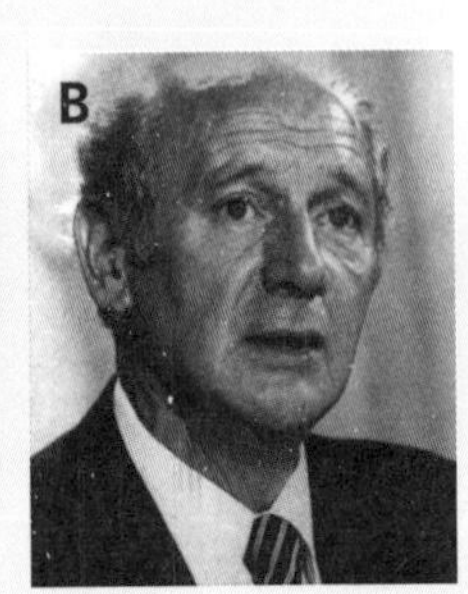

(i) Name each leader.

(ii) Name the party which each was leader of.

(iii) Put the five Taoisigh in chronological (time sequence) order.

(iv) Name which one of the leaders was Taoiseach at the time of the following events:
   (a) The Anglo-Irish Agreement, 1985
   (b) The International Oil Crisis, 1973-1974
   (c) Accession to the EEC, 1973
   (d) The New Programme for Economic Expansion, 1959
   (e) The Sunningdale Agreement, 1973
   (f) The Good Friday Agreement, 1998

## Question 2: DOCUMENTS

Study Documents **1, 2** and **3** below, and then answer the following questions.

### (a) Document 1

This is an extract from a speech made to the Irish public in January 1980 by the then Taoiseach, Charles Haughey.

*'I wish to talk to you this evening about the state of the nation's affairs and the picture I have to paint is not, unfortunately, a very cheerful one. The figures which are now just becoming available to us show one thing very clearly. As a community we are living away beyond our means. I do not mean that everyone in the community is living too well. Clearly many are not and have barely enough to get by. But taking us all together, we have been living at a rate which is simply not justified by the amount of goods and services we are producing. To make up the difference, we have been borrowing enormous amounts of money, borrowing at a rate which just cannot continue. A few simple figures will make this very clear.*

*At home, the government's current income from taxes and all other sources in 1979 fell short of what was needed to pay the running costs of the state by about £520m million. To meet this and our capital programme, we had to borrow in 1979 over £1,000 million. That amount equals to one-seventh of our entire national output. The situation in regard to our trading with the outside world in 1979 was bad also. Our income from abroad fell short of what we had to pay out by about £760 million which led to a fall in our reserves.*

*To fully understand our situation, we must look not just on the home scene but also on the troubled and unstable world around us. There are wars and rumours of wars. There is political instability in some of the most important areas of the world. A very serious threat exists to the world's future supply of energy. We can no longer be sure that we will be able to go on paying the prices now being demanded for all the oil and other fuels we require to keep our factories going and to keep our homes and institutions supplied with light, heat and power they need. We will, of course push exploration for our own oil ahead as rapidly as possible but in the short term the burden of oil prices will continue to be a crushing one.*

*All this indicates that we must, first of all, as a matter of urgency, set about putting our domestic affairs in order and secondly, improving our trade with the rest of the world in so far as we can do so. We will have to continue to cut down on government spending. The government is taking far too much by way of taxes from individual members of the community. But even this amount is not enough to meet our commitments. We will just have to reorganise government spending so that we can only undertake the things which we can afford.'*

(i) What does Haughey mean by the phrase 'living away beyond our means'?

(ii) How much is the shortfall between the running costs of the state and the money the government is receiving from taxes and all other sources in 1979?

(iii) How much will the government have to borrow in 1980?

(iv) What international crisis is causing difficulties for the running of Ireland's factories and homes?

(v) How does Haughey propose to solve the difficulties facing the country?

(vi) Explain the term 'budget deficit'.

## (b) Document 2

The following is an extract from an article written by journalist Brían Ó hUiginn, published in *The Irish Press*, 7 April 1949.

'It is said that a brisk trade is being done in the sale of bunting to be used on Easter Sunday when the 26 counties government with the approval of the 26 counties Dáil and presumably the benediction of the 26 Counties President will declare the 26 Counties a Republic.

The whole business is bunkum pure and simple. The Republic of Ireland was proclaimed in arms on Easter Monday 1916. After an All-Ireland election contest, representatives of the whole country met in Dáil Éireann on January 21, 1919, when the Republic was established in the most solemn manner and its Declaration of Independence sent out to the nations.

It has never since been disestablished; the Declaration of Independence has never been revoked. Hundreds of men and women have given their lives in defence of the Republic of Ireland; thousands have suffered imprisonment, hunger, torture, poverty and exile because of their fidelity to it; Irish people the world over have been stirred and inspired and edified by the unselfish devotion of its loyal adherents.

It has been suppressed by force for the past 27 years (1922) and at times under coercion enactments, the very name of it has been declared illegal. Why is that suppression not being removed now, the Republic of Ireland, restored, and peace and unity and national self-respect re-established in our midst?

Why set up the scarecrow of a 26 Counties Republic decorated with bunting to make as many people as possible believe that it is what it seems to be?

A little humanity, a little honesty, a little respect for the truth, a little real statesmanship, a little courage would wipe out all the bitterness of 27 years and encourage the best of our young people to go forward bravely and joyously to the final crowning of their country's nationhood.

Bunting and bunkum will never do it.'

(i) What does the author believe will happen on Easter Sunday?

(ii) When was the Republic first proclaimed?

(iii) When was the Republic then established 'in the most solemn manner'?

(iv) What has been happening 'for the past 27 years' according to this article?

(v) Why do you think that the author would describe the declaration of the Republic as a 'scarecrow of a 26 Counties Republic'?

(vi) Is the author supportive of the Irish government's decision to declare an Irish Republic? Give reasons for your answer using evidence from the document.

## (c) Document 3

The following is a summary of the election results from the Irish general elections of 1951 and 1954.

| Party | 1951 | 1954 |
|---|---|---|
| Fianna Fáil | 68 | 65 |
| Fine Gael | 40 | 50 |
| Labour Party | 16 | 18 |
| Clann na Talmhán | 6 | 5 |
| Clann na Poblachta | 2 | 3 |
| Independents | 14 | 5 |
| Ceann Comhairle | 1 | 1 |

(i) How many seats did Fianna Fáil lose at the 1954 election?

(ii) Which party gained the most seats from 1951 to 1954?

(iii) In 1954, the second Inter-Party Government was made up of Fine Gael, the Labour Party and Clann na Talmhán. What was their Dáil majority over Fianna Fail?

(iv) Did Fianna Fáil have enough seats to gain an overall majority in 1951? Give details in your answer.

(v) Which party was Noel Browne a member of until 1951?

(vi) Outline two economic difficulties facing Irish governments during the 1950s.

## Question 3: SHORT-ANSWER QUESTIONS

(a) Explain the following terms:

(i) Coalition
(ii) Balance of payments
(iii) Budget deficit
(iv) Second Vatican Council
(v) The New Programme for Economic Expansion
(vi) Social Partnership

(b) Put the following Taoisigh in chronological (time sequence) order:
Albert Reynolds - Charles Haughey - Garret FitzGerald - Bertie Ahern - John Bruton

(c) Match the people in Column A with the correct event in Column B:

| Column A | Column B |
|---|---|
| 1 T. K. Whitaker | (a) Second Vatican Council |
| 2 Charles Haughey | (b) Introduction of Free Education |
| 3 Jack Lynch | (c) New Programme for Economic Expansion |
| 4 Donogh O'Malley | (d) Accession to the EEC |
| 5 Pope John XXIII | (e) Anglo-Irish (Hillsborough) Agreement, 1985 |
| 6 Garret FitzGerald | (f) Arms Trial |

(d) Using the words provided in the box below, fill in the following gaps.

**The First Inter-Party Government**

The First __________ Government of 1948 was a coalition of Fine _______, the Labour Party, Clann na ___________, Clann na Talmhán and the National Labour Party. John A _________ was made Taoiseach and Labour's William Norton became __________.

In April 1949 Costello declared Ireland to be a Republic and thus no longer part of the British ______________. The name of the country was changed from Éire to the Republic of Ireland. The ____________ Development Authority (IDA) was also set up during this time.

The Minister for Health, Noel ________, was a member of Clann na Poblachta and he managed to eradicate ____________ (TB) by setting up ___________, introducing mobile x-ray units and using a new vaccine called the BCG. He then tried to introduce free medical cover to all mothers and their children up to the age of 16. This was known as the __________ __________ __________ Scheme. It was resisted by the __________ Church who saw it as interference in family matters while doctors saw it as an end to doctor-patient privacy. Costello refused to support Browne and he resigned from government. Following further difficulties, the first Inter-Party government soon collapsed.

**Catholic – Costello – Commonwealth – sanatoria – Poblachta – Tánaiste – Industrial – Browne – Gael – tuberculosis – Inter-Party – Mother and Child**

(e) **Fianna Fáil in Power**

In 1951, F______________ F______________ won the election but in 1954 another election was called and the second I______________ -P______________ Government was elected.

Ireland was suffering from many economic difficulties: high un______________ and e______________ to Britain and America meant that another election was called in 1957.

In 1959, Seán L________ replaced de V______________ as Taoiseach and he introduced the New P______________ for E______________ E______________ which encouraged foreign companies to set up in Ireland.

Minister for Education, Donogh O'________ offered free secondary school education to all students and also free transport to and from school. This was a huge success.

In 1961 Ireland established its first national television service called T______________ É______________ .

Relations with Northern Ireland improved when Seán L______________ travelled north to meet the Northern Irish P______________ Minister, Terence O'______________ in 1965. In 1966, Jack L___________ replaced Seán L______________ as Taoiseach.

Ireland joined the EEC in 19______________ and the C______________ A______________ P______________ helped farmers double their incomes but also caused Irish fish stocks to be destroyed.

In 1973 Lynch signed the S______________ Agreement with British Prime Minister Edward H______________ . This created a power-s______________ government in Northern Ireland.

In 1974 two bombs in Dublin and M___________ killed 33 and injured over 300 people.

In 1969 two government ministers Charles H______________ and Neil B______________ were accused of importing arms into Ireland.

The 1980s were difficult times with high un_____________ causing increased levels of e__________ to the UK, Europe and America.

The A______________ -I______________ A______________ of 19______________ gave the Republic a say in the running of Northern Ireland.

The C______________ T______________ years of the 1990s saw full employment but rises in house prices and costs and a lack of regulation in the b__________ system caused new difficulties.

## Question 4:
## PEOPLE IN HISTORY

**Write an account of a political leader in the Republic of Ireland during the period 1949-1985 using the following guidelines or hints:**

HINTS:

* Early years
* Challenges
* Achievements

**Answer Guidelines [Seán Lemass]**

### Early years

- Born in Dublin 1899 he was involved in the 1916 Rising and fought in the War of Independence. He opposed the Treaty and fought against the Free State in the Civil War. He was one of the occupants of the Four Courts when it was bombed by Free State forces. Elected in 1924 as a member of Sinn Féin, he joined Fianna Fáil in 1926.
- During the Emergency, he was made Minister for Supplies. He organised the rationing of food and goods like sugar, butter and fuel. He also served as Minister of Industry and Commerce and finally as Tánaiste in 1945. He became Taoiseach in 1959 when Éamon de Valera resigned.

### Challenges

- Upon gaining leadership, Lemass gave up de Valera's policy of high tariffs and self sufficiency. Ireland had a balance of payments problem. It was importing far more goods than it was exporting and had to borrow money to buy these goods. This meant taxes were raised and less money was available for social care.
- Ireland was heavily reliant on agriculture and after World War II, there was very little employment.
- Emigration was at the highest level in decades and the population of the country was at its lowest in its history.

### Achievements

- Along with the Secretary of the Department of Finance, T.K. Whitaker, Lemass set up a new economic policy: The New Programme for Economic Expansion in 1959. This offered grants to farmers and business to produce goods more efficiently.
- He also encouraged foreign companies to set up in Ireland through grants and low taxes on profits. Shannon Town and Industrial Estate was established.
- The Anglo-Irish Free Trade Agreement of 1965 allowed goods to be exported to Britain without tariffs and Ireland reduced its tariffs on British goods by 10% every year. By 1975 there was total free trade between the two countries.
- The Minister for Education Donogh O'Malley introduced free secondary education, free transport to schools and grants to build new secondary schools. Telefís Éireann was launched on 31 December 1961.
- He changed the policy on Northern Ireland when he accepted an invitation by the Prime Minister of Northern Ireland, Terence O'Neill, to meet. He travelled to the North in 1965 and was the first Irish Taoiseach to meet a Northern Irish Prime Minister.
- Lemass resigned in 1966 and Jack Lynch replaced him as Taoiseach.

## Question 5:

(a) Examine the statistics below and answer the following questions:
(All figures are in thousands)

| Period | Total births | Total deaths | Natural increase | Change in population | Estimated net migration |
|---|---|---|---|---|---|
| 1926-1936 | 58 | 42 | 16 | 0 | -17 |
| 1936-1946 | 60 | 43 | 17 | -1 | -19 |
| 1946-1951 | 66 | 40 | 26 | 1 | -24 |
| 1951-1956 | 63 | 36 | 27 | -12 | -39 |
| 1956-1961 | 61 | 34 | 26 | -16 | -42 |
| 1961-1966 | 63 | 33 | 29 | 13 | -16 |
| 1966-1971 | 63 | 33 | 30 | 19 | -11 |
| 1971-1979 | 69 | 33 | 35 | 49 | 14 |
| 1979-1981 | 73 | 33 | 40 | 38 | -3 |
| 1981-1986 | 67 | 33 | 34 | 19 | -14 |
| 1986-1991 | 56 | 32 | 24 | -3 | -27 |
| 1991-1996 | 50 | 31 | 18 | 20 | 2 |
| 1996-2002 | 54 | 31 | 23 | 49 | 26 |

**Figures from the CSO**

(i) During which period is emigration at its highest?
(ii) Give two historical reasons for this.
(iii) List the three periods when there was inward migration (people coming into Ireland).
(iv) The period from 1961 to 1971 shows a reduction in emigration from Ireland. Give an historical explanation for this.
(v) Why was there a drop in the population for the first time in over 20 years during the period 1986-1991?
(vi) Which decade saw the greatest number of births?
(vii) What is notable about the number of deaths in each period over the years 1926-2002?

(b) Write an account on two of the following:
(i) The 1950s in Ireland
(ii) Fianna Fáil in power, 1957-1973.
(iii) The 1980s in Ireland
(iv) Noel Browne

Chapter 15

# NORTHERN IRELAND

## Question I: PICTURES

### (a) Picture A

**Look at the photos above and answer the following questions:**

(i) Name each of the people in the photos (A-G) above.

(ii) Name the political parties that the people in photographs A, B, D and E were leaders of.

(iii) Explain the connection between the leaders in photographs F and G.

## (b) Picture B

**Examine the map and answer the following questions:**

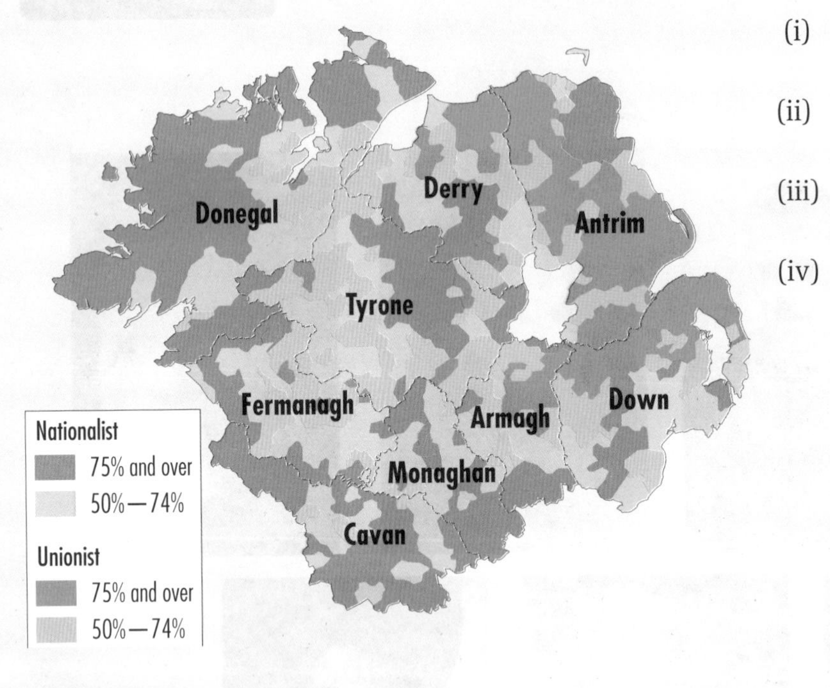


(i) Which counties make up Northern Ireland?

(ii) Which counties have a majority of nationalists?

(iii) Name the counties with a majority of unionists.

(iv) Explain why most of the unionists are located in the eastern half of Ulster.

## (c) Picture C

**Look at Picture C (showing British troops in Northern Ireland in 1969) and then answer the following questions.**

(i) How did Catholics and nationalists react at first to the arrival of British troops in Northern Ireland?

(ii) Give one reason why Catholics reacted in this way.

(iii) Look at Picture C and state whether this is a scene of street violence or not.

(iv) What do you think the soldiers are doing in Picture C? Give a reason for your answer.

(v) How did Catholics regard British troops after they had been in Northern Ireland for a few years?

## Question 2: DOCUMENTS

Study Documents **1** and **2** below and then answer the following questions.

### (a) Document 1

This is an extract from an article by journalist Nell McCafferty, written the day after Bloody Sunday and published in *The Irish Times* in January 1972.

'Three men died in a barricade which I vacated below the high flats in Rossville Street as four British Army tanks came rushing up the street. I ran into Colmcille court, a car park behind the maisonettes and burst into a woman's home. As I lay on the floor, shots rang out and there was a simultaneous knocking on the door as men cried: "For Jesus' sake, Missus, let us in, they're shooting."

'The woman of the house let them in and I heard more shots ring out. I looked out the window and beyond the picket fence of the back garden a man lay on the ground.

'Paratroopers had taken up position at the far end of the courtyard. They rushed forward and surrounded about 30 people who I had left at the gable wall giving entrance to the courtyard. Among the 30 arrested was a woman whom I watched protesting to the soldiers. A paratrooper struck her across the face with the butt of his rifle, placed his boot against her stomach, pushed her back against the wall and ordered her to follow the crowd of arrested men.'

(i) Where was the barricade where the three men had died located?

(ii) Who were the men referring to when they said, 'For Jesus' sake, Missus, let us in, they're shooting'? Give a reason for your answer.

(iii) What happened to the woman who protested to the paratroopers?

(iv) Why were the paratroopers rounding up the 30 people?

(v) From your reading on Bloody Sunday, how many protestors died that day?

## (b) Document 2

The following is an extract from the Downing Street Declaration of 1993.

*The Prime Minister, on behalf of the British Government, reaffirms that they will uphold the democratic wish of a greater number of the people of Northern Ireland on the issue of whether they prefer to support the Union or a sovereign united Ireland. On this basis, he reiterates [restates], on behalf of the British Government, that they have no selfish, strategic or economic interest in Northern Ireland. Their primary interest is to see peace, stability and reconciliation established by agreement among all the people who inhabit the island, and they will work together with the Irish Government to achieve such an agreement . . .*

(i) What are the possible 'democratic wishes' of the greater number of the people of Northern Ireland?

(ii) What is meant by the terms 'Union' and also the term 'united Ireland'?

(iii) Does the British Government want to keep Northern Ireland for any economic reason? Give reasons for your answer.

(iv) According to this Declaration, what is the primary interest of the British Government?

## Question 3: SHORT-ANSWER QUESTIONS

(a) Explain the following terms:

(i) Gerrymandering (iii) Internment (v) Unionist (vii) Articles 2 and 3
(ii) Sectarianism (iv) Loyalist (vi) Hunger Strike

(b) Explain how changing the election system from proportional representation to first-past-the-post discriminated against the nationalist community in the Northern Ireland.

(c) What powers did the Special Powers Act of 1922 give the government of Northern Ireland?

(d) Give two examples of government sectarianism in Northern Ireland during the early years of the Northern Ireland state.

(e) Name two of Northern Ireland's main industries in the first half of the twentieth century.

(f) Explain how the Education Act of 1947 could have contributed to the Troubles twenty years later.

(g) Give the full name of the following acronyms:

(i) RUC (iii) NICRA (v) UUP (vii) UVF
(ii) PIRA (iv) DUP (vi) SDLP (viii) IICD

(h) Fill in the gaps: rewrite the following sentences and fill in the missing words.

(i) The ______________________ of ______________ Act, 1920 created the state of Northern Ireland.

(ii) The new state of Northern Ireland was dominated by members of the U________ U __________ Party and the Prime Minister was James C______.

(iii) The police force in Northern Ireland was called the R______ U_______ C______________ and they were helped by the part-time force called the B-S_________. This part-time force was almost exclusively Protestant and discriminated against n____________.

(iv) The Northern Ireland government used g_______________ to make sure that more unionist candidates were elected than n__________.

(v) In 19___, a movement was established to promote political equality for Catholics and it was called the N__________ I______________ C__________ R________ Association.

(vi) The violence in Northern Ireland became known as the T__________. Many families were driven from their homes due to s___________ violence. Most of these were Catholic. This violence was particularly bad in an area in Derry called the B________.

(vii) John H_______, among others, established a new party called the S_____________ D_______________ and Labour Party.

(viii) Due to the increased violence, the new Northern Ireland Prime Minister Brian F______________ introduced i______________ (the arrest and imprisonment of suspects without trial).

(ix) In Derry on Sunday 30 January 1972, 13 unarmed marchers were killed in what became known as B_________ S______________ .

(x) The S________________ Agreement, 1973 between all the different parties, including the British and Irish governments, was reached to create a p________-s________________ government. The Agreement collapsed when many l________________ who opposed it went on strike.

(xi) B__________ S_______ was the first hunger s________ who died after 66 days. He was followed by another ____ people before the strike was called off.

(xii) After a number of agreements and declarations, the G________ F________ Agreement was signed in 19____. The Agreement was voted on in r___________ on both sides of the border.

(i) Explain what each of the following treaties agreed:

(i) Government of Ireland Act, 1920

(ii) Sunningdale Agreement, 1973

(iii) Anglo-Irish (Hillsborough) Agreement, 1985

(iv) The Good Friday Agreement, 1998

# Question 4: PEOPLE IN HISTORY

**Write an account of a person living in the nationalist area of Derry during the late 1960s and 1970s using the following hints or guidelines:**

HINTS:

* Political situation in Northern Ireland
* Discrimination
* Civil Rights Movement
* Some of the main marches and events

## The political situation in Northern Ireland

⇨ The Government of Ireland Act, 1920 created Northern Ireland. It consisted of six counties: Derry, Antrim, Down, Armagh, Fermanagh and Tyrone. The majority of people in these counties were unionist.

⇨ The city of Derry (or Londonderry as it is known among the unionists) had a majority of nationalists living in the city but due to gerrymandering they were represented by a unionist member of Parliament.

⇨ The Education Act, the National Health Service and pensions and unemployment assistance helped the poorer Catholic communities in Northern Ireland.

## Discrimination

⇨ Sectarian discrimination took place throughout Northern Ireland: Catholics were forced out of their homes but they could not go to the police because the RUC and the B-Specials were almost entirely Protestant.

⇨ The Special Powers Act also allowed for people to be imprisoned without any trials.

⇨ It was difficult to get any change as the elections were organised using first-past-the-post which favoured the larger unionist parties like the UUP.

⇨ Gerrymandering of constituency lines made sure that even in areas that had Catholic majorities, nationalists could not get their politicians elected.

⇨ It was difficult for Catholics to get a job in the Civil Service and when a Protestant employer had a choice, he or she often decided to employ another Protestant rather than a Catholic.

## The Civil Rights Movement

- The Northern Ireland Civil Rights Association (NICRA) was set up by a number of Catholics and Protestants who believed that the Catholic community was not receiving equal rights. They called for:
  - equality in housing, employment and education
  - the removal of the Special Powers Act
  - the end of gerrymandering
- Some of its leaders were Gerry Fitt, John Hume and Bernadette Devlin.

## Some of the main marches and events

- Further violence broke out after the creation of NICRA. The Battle of the Bogside (August 1969) in Derry was particularly violent.
- Following the violence, the British government sent the army into Northern Ireland to establish order. Some people believed the army would protect the Catholic communities but this belief quickly changed.
- In January 1972 a march against internment was organised in Derry. The British army tried to stop the march and clashes took place. By the end of Bloody Sunday 13 unarmed marchers had been shot and killed by the British army.

## Question 5:

**(a)** Write a paragraph about two of the following:

**(i)** The Hunger Strikes
**(ii)** The Sunningdale Agreement, 1973 and the loyalist strikes, 1974.
**(iii)** Internment, 1971
**(iv)** The Battle of the Bogside, 1969

**(b)** In 1969, the Taoiseach Jack Lynch stated on television 'it is clear that the Irish Government can no longer stand by and see innocent people injured and perhaps worse.'

**(i)** Why do you think he made this comment?
**(ii)** Do you think that the Irish government should have invaded Northern Ireland? Give reasons for your answer.

**(c)** Write an account of the role John Hume played in the Northern Ireland peace process.

# Chapter 16

# Ireland: Social History

## Question 1: Pictures

### (a) Picture A

### (b) Picture B

**Examine Pictures A and B and answer the questions that follow:**

(i) List two methods of transport shown in Picture A.
(ii) List two methods of transport shown in Picture B.
(iii) Give one method of transporting goods shown in Picture A.
(iv) From the two pictures, give one major change in the layout of O'Connell Street in Dublin.
(v) Name one thing that has changed in the way people dress.
(vi) Give one advantage and one disadvantage of the growth of car ownership in Ireland over the past 50 years.

## Question 2: DOCUMENTS

Study Documents **1** and **2** below and then answer the following questions.

### (a) Document 1

This is an extract describing life in Dublin tenements in the 1930s from a story by Terry Fagan, author and historian.

*There was poverty everywhere we looked in this neighbourhood. Some people had to live in the most deplorable conditions I'd ever seen. There were people with ten, twelve and in some cases fourteen children living in one room with no water, light or gas. That was real hardship. There were lots and lots of tenement houses around the neighbourhood. We survived in them and paid a big price. Death was a common thing in the tenements. My own sister's two young children died in those rotten rat-infested tenements. She put them to bed one night and the next morning both were dead. We call it 'cot deaths' today. The doctor was called. Sure all he did was to pronounce them dead and left.*

*I blame the deplorable conditions we had to live in for their deaths. I remember her husband and another man going over across the road to Farrell's undertakers in Corporation Street, where they made the coffins. They bought two little white coffins for a couple of shillings. There was no such thing as funeral parlours in those days. I remember them carrying the two coffins across the street and into the room. They put the two children's bodies into them. Then they put each coffin into a white pollyass that was used to stuff straw into to make a mattress to lie on. That's all people had to sleep on in the tenements was straw. No such thing as spring mattresses or anything like that. They then carried each coffin covered in the white pollyass down to the street. They then put the two coffins onto the crossbar of two bikes and cycled all the way out to Glasnevin Cemetery, for their little bodies to be buried in the Angels' plot.*

*I remember there wasn't a day went by when I'd see people being carried out of their houses in coffins. They were after dying from TB or some other sickness. The undertaker done a roaring trade in the area, as there was always someone dying in the neighbourhood from TB. Death was a regular thing in the neighbourhood when I was growing up. The people of this neighbourhood are strong people. They had it very hard in years gone by, with bad working conditions, bad housing, bad health and death. They had it all on their doorsteps. Day in and day out and they survived to tell the tale.*

(i) How many children could be living in each of the rooms?

(ii) How did the author's sister's two children die?

(iii) How did the men bring the two coffins to the cemetery?

(iv) Give an example of a disease that caused death in the tenements.

(v) What changes in housing took place in the years between 1930 and 1960 to help solve the problems of the tenements?

## (b) Document 2

This is an extract from an account describing life in Tuam, County Galway in the 1950s. This extract is taken from the book *Are Ye the Band? – A Showband Memoir* written by Jimmy Higgins.

1956 was a year that was to leave a lasting impression on me as a ten-year-old youngster. It was the year that Galway won the All-Ireland football final and I remember being in the Square in Tuam to welcome home the team with the Sam Maguire Cup. They were led by three Tuam men: captain Jack Mangan and 'the terrible twins', Sean Purcell and Frankie Stockwell.

It was also the year that Russian tanks rolled into Budapest resulting in a young trumpeter, Joe Chebi, escaping from Hungary and moving to the west to eventually settle in Dublin where he worked for many years as principal trumpeter with the National Symphony Orchestra.

Also on 1 December 1956, Ronnie Delaney won a gold medal for Ireland in Melbourne. But most importantly for me, 1956 was the year that I joined the Tuam Brass and Reed Band – in the trumpet section.

Unlike a lot of provincial towns, Tuam was fortunate in having a musical teacher of the calibre of bandmaster Mr Danny Kelly in its midst. He produced some fine players, and it was no great surprise to see that many of them went on to play with some of the top showbands in the country including the Army and Garda bands.

(i) Having read this extract, do you think that sport was important to people living in rural Ireland in the 1950s? Give <u>two</u> reasons for your answer.

(ii) State four reasons why the author remembers the year 1956. Which reason is the most important to the author? Explain why.

(iii) Do you think the author was aware of what was happening in the world outside Ireland in the 1950s? Give two reasons for your answer.

(iv) Why did trumpeter Joe Chebi flee from Hungary and end up spending his life in Ireland?

(v) From the extract, list <u>two</u> pastimes that were popular in rural Ireland in the 1950s.

(vi) According to the author, how was Tuam different, in at least one way, from other rural Irish towns in the 1950s?

## Question 3: SHORT-ANSWER QUESTIONS

(a) Explain the following terms:

(i) Thatch roofs
(ii) Súgán chair
(iii) *Meitheal*
(iv) Telegraph
(v) Trams
(vi) 2RN
(vii) Suffrage
(viii) Urban renewal schemes
(ix) Corporation houses
(x) Telephone exchange

(b) Using the photos shown here as a help, give a description of the rural housing of the following people in 1900:

**A** A rich landlord

**B** A wealthy farmer

**C** A small farmer

**D** A farm labourer

(c) Outline the differences between the various types of housing of people living in cities.

(d) Look at the statistics for the percentage of people living in one- or two-roomed houses in 1926 and 1946 and explain what this shows us about the wealth of the population of Ireland.

| | Dublin | Cork | Limerick |
|---|---|---|---|
| **1926** | 50% | 28% | 39% |
| **1946** | 25% | 21% | 23% |

(e) Using the words provided in the box below, fill in the following gaps.

In the early years of the 20th__________ , most journeys were taken by foot or using bicycles, donkeys or horse-and –__________ . The roads between towns were not very good and in big cities cobblestones were used in the streets.

In the big cities of Belfast, Dublin and Cork, electric__________ transported people around. Longer journeys were taken by steams __________ . Cars became more popular after World War II. Any journeys abroad were taken by ship from ports such as__________ (Dún Laoghaire), Queenstown (__________) and Belfast.

Things began to change from the 1960s onwards. Cars became more affordable and thus more popular. Trams were replaced by__________ and new and improved roads linked the cities together. Problems with traffic__________ in Dublin finally resulted in trams being re-introduced.

Ferries across to Britain and mainland Europe have become quicker and more comfortable. __________ __________ has become much cheaper and now millions of people fly in and out of Ireland every year.

**Cobh, trams, air travel, congestion, century, train, carts, buses, Kingstown**

(f) Write a point about the impact on Irish life of the following changes in communication since 1960:

(i) Telegraphs (iii) Facsimile (v) Mobile phones
(ii) Telephones (iv) Computer (vi) The Internet

(g) Match each item in Column A with its explanation in Column B:

| Column A | Column B |
|---|---|
| 1 Intermediate Education Act, 1878 | (a) Banned any discrimination based on gender or marital status |
| 2 Marriage ban | (b) Tried to gain support for female suffrage |
| 3 Conditions of Employment Act, 1935 | (c) Allowed women to sit examinations |
| 4 Employment Equality Act, 1977 | (d) Forced women to give up their jobs in the civil service when they got married |
| 5 Commission on the Status of Women | (e) Allowed women to take university degrees |
| 6 Irish Women's Franchise League, 1908 | (f) Recommended 49 ways to eradicate gender inequality |
| 7 Royal University of Ireland Act, 1879 | (g) Allowed government to limit number of women in any industry |

(h) Using the words provided in the box below, fill in the following gaps.

(i) **Early Years**
The majority of people in Ireland at the beginning of the twentieth century worked in agriculture. Most of the farming was ________ farming which required a lot of manual work. Fields had to be ploughed, sown and the harvest gathered using _______-drawn machinery. Neighbouring farmers would help each other gather in the harvest using ________. This cooperation was called ________.

(ii) **Changes**
Motorised __________ replaced horses which reduced the time taken for fields to be ___________ and sown. ___________ ___________ and other machines further helped the farmer. Farms grew bigger and many moved towards __________ farming. The entry of Ireland into the _______ and the help from the CAP and the ________ ________ helped to raise the standard of living of farmers.

***Meitheal*, livestock, tillage, scythes, Social Fund, horse, tractors, EEC, ploughed, combine harvesters**

(i) Look at the table shown here and answer the questions that follow:

| | % Of Workers Employed In Each Sector | | |
|---|---|---|---|
| | Agriculture | Industry | Services |
| 1926 | 53 | 13 | 34 |
| 1971 | 26 | 31 | 43 |
| 1996 | 10 | 27 | 63 |

(i) In what sector of employment did the majority of people work in 1926?
(ii) What sector of employment had the largest percentage growth between 1926 and 1971?
(iii) Which sector had the largest number of people working in it in 1996?
(iv) Why do you think industry has never been the largest sector of employment?
(v) Outline the historical reasons for the decline in employment in agriculture over the twentieth century.

(j) Place the following items or events into the correct period of time:
(a) Internet
(b) The era of the Showbands
(c) First broadcast of RTÉ television
(d) Raves
(e) Opening of the Abbey Theatre
(f) Beginning of 2RN – Ireland's first radio station
(g) First cinema in Ireland
(h) Ireland in the soccer World Cup

| 1900-1925 | 1925-1950 | 1950-1975 | 1975-2000 |
|---|---|---|---|

## Question 4: PEOPLE IN HISTORY

**Write an account of the changes that have occurred for a woman living in Ireland during the twentieth century, using the following headings or hints as a guide:**

HINTS:

* Education
* Right to vote
* Changes in employment legislation
* Political status

### Education

➪ At the beginning of the twentieth century very few women were encouraged to go to university. It was only with the Intermediate Education Act of 1878 that women were allowed to sit state exams!

➪ In 1879, women were finally allowed to take university degrees although they were not allowed into the campuses. By 1900, 417 women had arts degrees and 25 had medical degrees.

➪ In 1904 Trinity College allowed women onto the campus to attend lectures and by 1908 all universities in Ireland admitted women.

➪ 1950 = 25% of all students in university were women. 1998 = 55%

### Right to vote

➪ Hanna Sheehy-Skeffington helped to set up the Irish Women's Franchise League (IWFL) in 1908 and before that, the Dublin Women's Suffrage Association in 1896.

➪ These groups protested and attacked buildings in an attempt to gain support for the suffragette movement. Sheehy-Skeffington and 36 others were arrested and went on hunger strike in order to gain political-prisoner status.

➪ A member of Cumann na mBan, Countess Markievicz was second-in-command of the troops at St. Stephen's Green during the 1916 Rising.

➪ In 1918, women over the age of 30 were given the right to vote and Markievicz was the first woman to be elected as a Member of Parliament. She was also made a Minister in the first Dáil.

➪ The 1922 Constitution gave men and women over the age of 21 the right to vote.

## Changes in employment legislation

- Women were limited to a number of jobs: mostly National School teachers and domestic service (cleaners, maids etc).

**Problems:**

- De Valera passed the marriage ban – a law in 1932
- The Conditions of Employment Act, 1935
- Trade Unions pushed for higher wages for men
- The 1937 Constitution gave women a special role 'within the home'.

**Changes:**

- National Council of Women and the Irish Women Workers' Union
- Commission on the Status of Women, 1972
- Marriage Ban lifted
- Employment Equality Act, 1977

## Political Status

- Still under-represented
- 1998: only 5% of university professors were women
- 1998: only 16% of judges were women
- 1998: only 12% of the Dáil were women
- Mary Robinson was the first woman to be President in 1990, followed by Mary McAleese in 1997

## Question 5:

**(a) (i)** Identify <u>three</u> types of primary sources that a historian could use to find out about social history in Ireland in the twentieth century.

**(ii)** Give <u>three</u> changes that have occurred in the following areas in Ireland in the twentieth century:

**1** Urban housing
**2** Rural life
**3** Leisure time

**(b)** Look at the following statistics on Irish general elections and answer the questions that follow:

| Year | Number of Candidates | Female candidates | Total number of seats | Dáil seats won by women | Women TDs as % of total number elected |
|---|---|---|---|---|---|
| 1969 | 373 | 11 (2.9%) | 144 | 3 | 2.1% |
| 1981 | 404 | 41 (10.1%) | 166 | 11 | 6.6% |
| 1987 | 466 | 58 (12.4%) | 166 | 14 | 8.4% |
| 1989 | 370 | 51 (13.7%) | 166 | 13 | 7.8% |

(i) In which year was the highest percentage of female candidates?
(ii) What is the increase in female representation between 1969 and 1989?
(iii) In which year was the highest number of women elected as a percentage of total deputies?
(iv) What are the historical reasons for such a low level of female representation in the Dáil?
(v) What changes could be made to make the representation more equal?

# 1 What Is History? – Revision Summary

## Work of a Historian

**Skills needed:**
1 **Looking** at items in museums
2 **Reading** and **checking** books
3 **Researching** the internet and libraries
4 **Interviewing** people
5 **Examining** photos, videos and films
6 **Asking** a lot of **questions**

## Sources

**Primary Sources:** information taken directly from the past. For example:
1 **Newspapers**
2 **Government records** like the Central Statistics Office's Census of the Population
3 **Diaries** of people
4 **Correspondence** (e.g. letters/ emails)
5 **Speeches** of people
6 **Interviews** with people about their experiences
7 **Photographs** of people and places
8 **Paintings** and **posters**: before the camera, people painted what they saw
9 **Autobiographies:** books written by someone about their lives.

**Secondary Sources:** information taken at a later time than the event being researched. For example:
1 **A biography:** a book written about someone by someone else.
2 **History books** are written by people who were not at the events they write about.
3 TV or radio **documentaries:** these describe what happened in the past.

**Problems** with sources: some sources are not always reliable. For example:
1 **Bias:** when people describe someone or something with some prejudice (like or dislike).
2 **Propaganda:** information or rumours created or spread to influence people
3 **Exaggeration:** stating that something is more or less/ bigger or smaller/ better or worse, that it really is.
4 **Accuracy:** some sources can just be wrong. That is why they need to be checked.

## Timelines

**Chronology:** the process of putting things in the order in which they happened.
Time is divided into hours/ days/ years/ decades/ centuries/ millennia.
Any year before Jesus was born is known as **BC (before Christ)** or **BCE (Before the Common Era)**.
Any year after Jesus was born is known as **AD (Anno Domini)** (in the year of our Lord) or **CE (Common Era)**.
Second 100 years before Jesus is the 2nd century BC
First 100 years after Jesus is the 1st century AD
**Periods or Ages:** some centuries are known as periods, e.g. The Stone Age was 2,500,000 BC until 2000 BC and people used stones to make tools.

## Archaeology (study of ancient things)

Archaeologists seek **artefacts** (objects from the past that are found in the ground)
Artefacts are found because: **1** People lose things **2** People hide things **3** Things are buried alongside people **4** Towns are emptied through disease or decline or are destroyed by volcanoes.

**How are they found:**

1 **By chance:** farmers often dig up artefacts such as the Ardagh Chalice.
2 **Geophysics and metal detectors** help archaeologists to find artefacts.
3 **Rescue archaeology:** when a road or new building is built over an old site.
4 **Old stories:** The city of Troy was found based on a story of the *Iliad*.
5 Seen from above: **soil patterns** show where a fort or town once existed.

**Excavation** or **dig:** place where archaeologists look for artefacts.
**Tools** needed: **pickaxes** and **trowels** for digging/**brushes** for removing dirt from artefact/**sieves** to find all artefacts/**drawing pad** and pencil to record position of artefact/**camera** to photograph dig/**site book** for cataloguing artefacts.

**Methods of dating:**

1 **Stratigraphy:** by locating an item at a certain level of the earth, it is possible to date the artefacts found at that level.
2 **Carbon dating:** all living things have carbon in them. It fades at a steady level. The older a thing, the less carbon it has. This helps date things that once lived.
3 **Dendrochronology:** all wooden artefacts have a ring pattern from the tree they were cut from. It is possible to record the pattern of the rings on trees from certain areas.
4 **Bones of skeleton:** DNA from bones, skin and hair fragments can give information. The actual skeleton can give clues to the height/gender/diet and even the death of the person.

# 2 Ancient Ireland – Revision Summary

## Stone Age Ireland

**Mesolithic Age: 8000 BC until 3500 BC** (meso = middle; lith = stone)
Food: **Hunter-gatherers:** they hunted birds and animals and gathered fruit, nuts and berries.
Tools: used **microliths** (micro = small), sharpened stone, wood, antler and bone to make weapons and tools. Wore animal skins.
Houses: round tepee-style huts: young trees planted in a circle and bent into centre with skins or grasses on the outside. Used fireplace (hearth-) stones to cook.
Burial tombs: none found
Location: Mount Sandal in County Derry

**Neolithic Age: 3500 BC until 2000 BC** (neo = New)
Food: Farmers grew barley and wheat, had livestock – cattle/pigs/goats/sheep and hunted wild animals.
Tools: Stone axes/ploughs/mattocks/bone needles and made pottery.
Houses: rectangular; made from stone, timber or wattle and daub. Hearth was in centre of house.
Burial tombs: Megalithic tombs (mega = large).
**Court-cairns:** open entrance (court) leads to circular room (cairn) where body and grave-goods were located.
**Dolmens:** three upright stones supporting massive **capstone.**
**Passage tombs:** long passage into central chamber with domed roof built with **corbelled** roof. **Roof-box** allowed winter solstice sun in. **Kerbstones** used outside.
Locations: Céide Fields, County Mayo; Lough Gur, County Limerick; Kilclooney, County Donegal (Dolmen); Newgrange, County Meath (Passage tomb)

## Bronze Age (2000 BC until 500 BC)

Food: Farmers grew barley and wheat for porridge and bread, had livestock. Used **fulacht fiadh** to cook outside.

Tools: Bronze pots, swords and sickles. Quern stones used to grind cereals. Gold **lunulae, torcs** and **dress fasteners.**
Houses: rectangular or circular using wattle and daub with thatch roof. Had walls around houses for protection.
Burial tombs: (i) **Wedge tombs:** large stone at an angle with small stones supporting
(ii) **Cist graves:** grave with stones around body and flat stone placed over it
(iii) **Standing stones - monoliths** (mono = one) or stone circles
Locations: The Burren, County Clare (wedge tombs), Church Bay, Rathlin Island (cist graves), Drombeg, County Cork (standing stones).

### Iron Age / Celtic Ireland (500 BC until AD 400)

Food: Farmers had livestock especially cattle, grew crops. Drank beer and mead.
Jewellery: **torcs, brooches** and **necklaces** all in **La Tène** Celtic style.
Houses: lived in: (i) **ringforts** (rath/lios/caiseal/cathir/dún) had a **fosses** (ditch) dug around the bank and a souterrain underneath. Emain Macha, County Armagh.
(ii) **Hillforts** – Tara, County Meath
(iii) **Promontory forts** – Dún Aengus, Aran Islands, County Galway
(iv) **Crannóg** – Ferrycarrig, County Wexford
Society: Divided into 150 **tuatha** (kingdoms) each with **rí** (king) and a **derbfine** (royal family).
The **Aos Dána: brehons** (judges)/**druids** (priests)/**filí** (bards)/craftsmen
Women could own property and were independent, e.g. Queen Medb/Boudicca
Pastimes: *Báire,* story-telling and board games like *ficheall* and *brandubh*
Burial customs: cist graves with **Ogham** stones. Believed in afterlife in Tír na nÓg.
Religion:
- Druids performed religious ceremonies.
- Major gods: Dagda/Roann/Lug
- estivals: Samhain/Imbolg/Bealtaine/Lughnasa

### Early Christian Ireland (Fifth century AD to Eleventh century AD)

Christianity in Ireland: **St. Patrick**/St. Secundius/St. Auxillius converted population
Monasteries set up: Kildare (St. Brigid)/**Clonmacnoise** (St. Ciarán)/**Clonfert** (St. Brendan) / Iona (St. Colmcille). Most spectacular: **Sceilig Mhichíl,** County Kerry.
The monastery: e.g. Glendalough, County Wicklow
Buildings: **Oratory** (monks attend mass and pray), **refectory** (monks eat their meals), **beehive huts** (where they lived), **scriptorium** (scribes copied manuscripts), **round towers** (used as bell towers or safe place if attacked).
Work of monks: abbot was head of monastery and he decided jobs, e.g. farming, cooking to feed other monks.
**Scribes** wrote **manuscripts** (handwritten books), e.g. Cathach/ Book of Durrow/ Book of Kells. Used **quills** to write on **vellum** or **parchment.**
Metal was worked for religious items, e.g. **chalices** of Ardagh and Derrynaflan/ Cross of Cong/ reliquaries to hold relics of saints like St. Patrick's Bell Shrine.
Stone masons carved **High Crosses,** e.g. Clonmacnoise, County Offaly.

## 3 Ancient Rome – Revision Summary

### Ancient Rome

**How do we know about Romans?**
**Archaeology:** remains of buildings and towns e.g. **Ostia, Antica** or **Pompeii** (destroyed when Mount Vesuvius erupted and covered the city in AD 79)

**Written accounts:** many could read and write Latin = many books, plays, poems and histories, e.g. Pliny/ Ovid/ Plautus/ Virgil

## Roman Society

Divided into patricians (aristocrats) and plebeians (professional and working class).
Houses: Wealthy people: **domus** built around **atrium** (open square) with **impluvium** (small pool) around which the bedrooms (**cubicula**)/ kitchens (**culina**) were built. **Peristylium** was a small walled garden at back. Poorer people lived in **insulae** (apartment blocks).
Clothes: Men wore a tunic and a toga and women wore a **stola** and a **palla.**
Food: **Cena** (main meal); ate meat/ seafood/ fruit. Poor ate **dole** (free grain from government) and ate at **thermopolia** (type of takeaway).
Education: age 7 children sent to **Ludus** – learnt reading and writing. Age 12 boys went to Grammaticus and learnt history/ literature/ grammar/ geometry/ arithmetic/ rhetoric and oration. Age 12 girls stayed at home and learnt how to run the home.
Women: very little freedom. Not allowed to vote or run for political position.
Slaves: slaves were taken from people captured in wars. Many were manual workers; educated slaves were doctors, teachers or secretaries. Slaves were generally treated badly but could be given **manumission** (freedom) from master.

## Entertainment

Baths, e.g. Baths of Diocletian: **caldarium** (hot room), **tepidarium** (warm room) and frigidarium (cold room) with **palaestra** (exercise area), libraries and gardens.
Chariot races: took place at **Circus Maximus** which held 200,000 people.
Gladiator fights: took place at **Colosseum** which held 70,000 people. Three types: **Samnite/ Thracian/ Retiarius.**
Theatre: Comedy plays by **Plautus** and **Terence** very popular.

## Religion

Major gods: Jupiter/ Neptune/ Pluto/ Venus/ Juno/ Mars.
Worshipped at temples, e.g. the **Pantheon.**
Believed in afterlife in Pluto's Underworld. **Elysian Fields** (heaven) and **Tartarus** (hell).
Funerals: cremated and placed in urns or in tombs. Tombs built along **Via Appia** outside city.
Christians persecuted and many lived in catacombs. **Emperor Constantine** converted to Christianity in fourth century.

## Roman Army

Used to control a large empire that stretched from Egypt to Britain and from Syria to Britain and Spain.
Divided into **legions** (usually about 4,000 to 5,000 soldiers).
Very disciplined: had to be able to march 32 kilometres a day. Carried all their equipment (40 kilograms).
Equipment: carried s**hield/ dagger/ pilum** (javelin), wore **greaves** (shin guards), chain mail over tunic and helmet.
Enemies: **Gauls** (French and Belgians)/ **Carthaginians** (in Africa)/ Germanic Tribes/ **Goths** who finally sacked Rome in AD 410.

## Legacy of Rome

1. **Engineering:** first in Europe to discover concrete and how to build the arch and domes.
2. **Aqueducts** carried water into the cities, e.g. Nimes in France.
3. **Roads:** 84,800 kilometres built using large stones on sand or gravel.

4 **Architecture:** Roman architecture of domes and columns still used today.
5 **Latin language:** basis of Portuguese / Spanish / French / Italian and Romanian.
6 **Calendar:** the Roman Julian calendar was used until the sixteenth century.
7 **Roman numerals:** I = 1, V = 5, X = 10, L = 50, C = 100, D = 500, M = 1,000.

# 4 The Middle Ages – Revision Summary

## Middle Ages (500 AD until 1400 AD)

**Feudal System**
Political, social and military system based on ownership of king and the holding of lands 'in fief' by his vassals.
King owned all land. King gave land to nobles who swore oath of loyalty, promised to pay money, provided knights to fight for king and provided hospitality to king if he came to visit.
Nobles then rented out land to lesser nobles or peasants in return for money.

## Castles

**Motte and bailey:** wooden walls with moat around it. Central area = bailey. Motte with keep on top where noble lived.
Stone castle: **stone curtain** walls with **turrets and ramparts** surrounded the bailey; **moat** outside stone walls; **gatehouse** had **portcullis** and a **drawbridge;** bailey had blacksmiths, workshops, kitchen, stables.
**Keep:** small windows; tapestries on walls. Great Hall was where business took place during day and feasts at night. **Chapel** for mass, **apartments** for sleeping, **solar** for pastimes of noble's wife.
Food: meat – boar, rabbit, hare, pork, beef, lamb, goose and pheasant. Very little vegetables; lots of spices and herbs; wine, mead or ale; eaten on a trencher.
Pastimes: hunting, hawking, tournaments for knights.
Women: arranged marriage; large dowry given with bride; spent time weaving, spinning and embroidery.
**Castle under attack:** attacking armies used scaling ladders, siege towers, battering rams, ballistas.

## Knight's Life: 3 stages of training

1. **Page:** age 7-14, learnt to read and write and acted as a servant at home of noble and lady. Basic training, riding and using a sword.
2. **Squire:** age 14-21, carried and looked after knight's armour and horse. Practised archery and fighting on horseback.
3. **Knight:** age 21, he was **dubbed.** Spent night praying, arrived at ceremony in morning dressed in armour. Promised to uphold code of chivalry. Spent his time as knight training and participating in **tourneys** (mock battles) and **jousting.**
   **Clothing:** weapons: lance/ sword/ axe/ mace/ hammer. Armour: helmet/ chain mail/ visor/ shield/ **gauntlet.**

## Country Life

Lesser nobles lived in manor house on a manor or grange.
**Manor:** bailiff's house/ peasants' houses/ church/ forest/ river/ craftsmen's houses/ farmland.
Peasant's life: two types: **freeman** (rented land from the noble) and **serf** (was owned by the noble and had to work on noble's land). Both had to pay tithe (tenth of crop to local priest).
Houses: wattle and daub houses with one or two rooms, dark and smoky.
Food: **pottage** (vegetable soup)/ eggs/ very little meat/ fruit and nuts from forest/ drank ale.
Work: worked on land. **Open Field Crop Rotation** meant they changed the crop in the three fields and left one fallow every third year. Used **sickles/ scythes** to cut crops and had to work on noble's farm a number of days each year.

Clothes: wool/ rough linen from flax/ dyes made from berries or plants/ shoes from leather
Pastimes: wrestling/ boardgames/ cockfighting and badger-baiting.

## Town Life

Towns were set up with charters from the king/ large stone walls with gates/ sentries guarded gates/ visitors had to pay a toll/ town hall and church were made of stone/ market square was at centre.
Annual fairs had exotic spices and cloth and took place outside town walls.
Houses made of wood = threat of fire. A **curfew** meant all fires had to be put out after dark.
Hygiene: rubbish and human waste was thrown into street. Typhoid, cholera and leprosy were common.
**Black Death** (Bubonic Plague) killed one-third of European population in fourteenth century.
**Guilds:** craftsmen set up guilds of their own craft, e.g. baker: only master-craftsmen allowed in guild and had to pay yearly fee to guild.
Training to be a master-craftsmen:

**Apprentice** age 12 learnt about trade for seven years without pay.
**Journeyman** (journée = day in French) apprentice who had learnt his trade could offer his work for payment.
**Master** had to produce a masterpiece – something to prove his skill/ability.
Punishment: bad craftsmen were carried through town on huddle/ ducking stool.

## Church architecture

**Romanesque:** Rounded doors and windows/ bell tower was square/ thick walls/ few windows/ big and rounded columns.
**Gothic:** thin walls/ flying buttresses/ thinner columns/ more windows/ **rose windows**/ pointed windows and doors/ tall spires/ **gargoyles.**

## Monastery Life

Monks followed rules of St. Benedict: had to promise to live in chastity/ poverty and obedience to abbot. Cut hair in tonsure.
Buildings: cloister (walled courtyard)/ refectory (where they ate)/ dormitory (where they slept)/ Chapter House (business took place)/ infirmary (where sick monks went)/ scriptorium (manuscripts written)/ Church.
New Orders: Dominicans/ Franciscans

## Ireland in Middle Ages

Vikings – eighth until eleventh century. Normans in eleventh century: **Diarmuid MacMurrough** invited **Strongbow** and Normans into Ireland. **Henry II – Lord of Ireland in 1172.**
Influence on Ireland:
1. New **castles** built – Carrickfergus, County Antrim
2. **Feudal system** introduced.
3. System of church **parishes**
4. New **names:** Fitz-, Butler etc.

# 5 The Renaissance – Revision Summary

## The Renaissance (= rebirth) 1400-1600

**Why in Italy?**
**1** Italian **city states** (Milan/ Florence/ Genoa/ Naples) became rich through trading with Asia.
**2** Rich **patrons** paid artists.
**3** **New ideas** from Asia.
**4** Italian language based on **Latin** so they could read old Roman texts.
**5** **Roman ruins** inspired Italians.
**6** The **Pope** lived in Rome. He had lots of wealth and power.
**7** The **sack of Constantinople** in 1453 by Muslims forced Greeks to flee and they brought old manuscripts back to Italy.

**How do we know about the Renaissance?**
Paintings, sculptures and pieces of art are in galleries around the world.
Artists' notebooks, letters and books.
Giorgio Vasari wrote a book called *Lives of the Artists.*

## Florence and the de Medici family

The de Medicis owned the wealthiest bank in Europe and controlled Florence.
**Cosimo de Medici** (1389-1464) first great patron. Got Brunelleschi to design dome of Santa Maria del Fiore.
Lorenzo the Magnificent (1449-1492) began **Platonic Academy**/ hired **da Vinci, Michelangelo, Botticelli.** Died and the city declined in power.

**Differences between Medieval and Renaissance Art**
**Subjects:** mostly religious versus classical stories, religious and portraits.
**Realistic:** cartoon-like characters versus real images of how people look.
**Perspective:** flat image versus things smaller when further away (vanishing point).
**Materials:** water and egg-yolk paint on wooden panels versus oil paint on canvas/ frescoes.
**Architecture:** Gothic style versus return to Romanesque columns/ pediments and domes.
**Sculpture:** abstract and connected to walls versus realistic and free-standing.

## Italian Artists

Leonardo da Vinci (1452-1519)
Born in Vinci, became apprentice to Verrocchio age 14 and studied art. Moved to Milan in 1482 to work for Duke Ludovico Sforza but moved to Rome in 1513 and then France in 1519. Died aged 57.
**Painted: The Virgin on the Rocks/ The Last Supper/ Mona Lisa**
**Invented and designed:** submarines/ helicopters/ weapons. Had great interest in anatomy and dissected over 30 bodies.
Michelangelo Buonarotti (1475-1564)
Born in Caprese near Florence, he moved to Florence and into the palace of the de Medicis. After death of Lorenzo he moved to Bologna and then Rome in 1494. He worked in Florence and Rome until his death aged 89.
Sculpture: ***The Pietà*** in Rome and ***David*** in Florence.
Painting: frescoes: **Sistine Chapel/ The Last Judgement**
Architecture: **St Peter's Dome** in Rome
Raphael Sanzio (1483-1520)
Born in Umbria, between Florence and Rome, worked for Pope Julius II and died in Rome aged 37.
Painting: ***Marriage of the Virgin*** and a fresco in Vatican Palace called ***The School of Athens.***

## Artists outside Italy

Rembrandt Harmenszoon van Rijn (1606-1669)
Born in **Leiden** and moved to Amsterdam in 1631. Married and had four children with Saskia van Uylengurg. He was declared bankrupt in 1656 and had to sell his house. He died aged 63 and was buried in an unmarked grave in Amsterdam.
Paintings: many paintings, drawings and etchings, ***The Night Watch.***

## Printing Press

Johann Gutenberg (c. 1400-1468)
He is thought to have invented the **moveable-type printing press** in 1450. Small metal letters placed into a frame and then pressed onto paper. First book was **Gutenberg Bible.**
**Results of printing press:**
**1.** Books became **cheaper** so more people bought books.
**2. More access** to books meant more people learnt to read.
**3. New ideas** spread as people read more.
**4.** Authors began to write in **vernacular** (everyday language) instead of Latin.

## Writers

**William Shakespeare** (1564-1616)
Born in **Stratford-on-Avon** in England in 1564. Married **Anne Hathaway** and had three children. He moved to London and wrote plays.
He was part-owner of theatrical company called **The King's Men** and opened a theatre called **The Globe** beside the Thames. Moved back to Stratford and died there aged 52.
Writings: 38 plays including tragedies: ***Hamlet, Romeo and Juliet, Macbeth*** and ***King Lear,*** histories: ***Julius Caesar, Henry V*** and comedies: ***Comedy of Errors*** and ***Twelfth Night.*** 154 sonnets and a number of poems.
Niccolò Machiavelli (1469-1527)
Born and died in Florence.
**Writings: *The Prince, On the Art of War*** and ***A History of Florence.***

## Medicine

Andreas Vesalius (1514-1564)
Born in Brussels, Belgium, he studied in University of Paris and then moved to Padua in Italy. Advanced **the study of anatomy.**
**Works:** wrote and illustrated ***On the Structure of the Human Body.***

## Science

Nicolaus Copernicus (1473-1543)
Born in Torun in Poland, he believed that the earth and the planets circle the sun.
Works: wrote ***On the Revolution of Heavenly Bodies.***
Galileo Galilei (1564-1642)
Born in Pisa, he taught at Universities of Pisa and Padua.
Believed all things could be explained through mathematics, that objects fall to earth at the same speed and that Copernicus was right.
He was asked to appear before **Inquisition**, was forced to withdraw his opinions and was put under house arrest in Florence where he died.

**Works:** wrote ***Dialogue on the Two Chief World Systems,*** made his own telescope to look at moon and stars including the moon's mountains and craters and the moons around Jupiter.

### Results of the Renaissance

1 **New Discoveries:** Inventions and greater knowledge in medicine, science, geography and printing press helped to spread news of the discoveries.
2 **Humanism:** the growth of the importance of the individual and thus the questioning of Church teachings and ideas.
3 **Spread of Knowledge:** The printing press, new and cheaper and more widely available books spread information and knowledge. Literacy also increased.
4 **Spread of ideas:** with greater literacy and interest in knowledge came ideas that were popular in the ancient world: democracy, republicanism and freedom for people.
5 **Art:** some of the greatest pieces of art were produced during the Renaissance.

## 6 Age of Exploration – Revision Summary

### Age of Exploration

**Causes**

1 Trade with east – for spices, jewels and silks – used the **Great Silk Route.** The spices from the **Spices Islands (Moluccas)** were very valuable.
2 In 1453, the fall of Constantinople to the Turks made travelling the Great Silk Route very dangerous so a new route was necessary.
3 A desire to expand **Christianity** and defeat Muslims in North Africa and the Middle East.
4 Monarchs wanted to expand their empires.
5 Explorers had read about travels of Marco Polo and were very excited.

### Advances in Travel

Maps: **cartographers** produced more detailed maps. Portuguese used ***portolan*** (harbour-finding) maps.
Navigation: along with compasses, new instruments like **quadrants** and **astrolabes** helped. Speed was measured by **knots,** depth by **fathoms** and all this was recorded in a logbook.
Ships: Portuguese and Spanish used strong **clinker-built ships.** Italians used manoeuvrable lateen ships. The Portuguese finally invented the **caravel** which used both the triangular sails of the lateen with the square sails of the clinker-built. It was both strong and manoeuvrable. Larger caravels were known as **naos** or **carracks.**

### Life on a Ship

Ate dried or salted food; **ship biscuit** and water often went putrid.
Poor diet meant sailors suffered from **typhoid** as a result of dirty water and **scurvy** from lack of vitamin C.
Living conditions were cramped and many died.

### Portugal begins

**Why?**

1 Portugal faced into the Atlantic.
2 Heard stories of great wealth in Africa from the Moors.
3 Advances in travel by Portuguese helped.

Prince Henry the Navigator (1394-1460): set up navigational school at **Sagres** (1420). His explorers placed padroas (stone pillars) along coastline. By his death Portugal had got as far as **Cape Bojador.**
Bartholomew Diaz (1450-1500): sailed around the southernmost point on Africa and named it **Cape**

**of Storms.** King John II of Portugal changed the name to **Cape of Good Hope.**
Vasco da Gama (1469-1524): travelled with four ships and travelled around the Cape and landed in **Natal** on Christmas Day. Travelled along African coast before sailing to Calicut in India.

**Results of Portuguese travels:**
1 Portugal became wealthier through trade.
2 Established an empire and created colonies along African coast.
3 Other countries tried to follow.

## Spain follows

Christopher Columbus (1451-1506)
Born in **Genoa,** Italy. After reading map of **Toscanelli,** he estimated **Cipangu** (Japan) and Cathay (China) were close enough to sail to by going west.
Received financial support from Spanish **King Ferdinand** and **Queen Isabella.**
The ships **Nina, Pinta** and **Santa Maria** sailed on 3 August 1492. Arrived 12 October and named the land San Salvador.
Explored neighbouring islands of **Cuba** and **Hispaniola.** Leaving 40 men behind, he returned to Spain.
Made three more journeys to the 'Indies' and 'discovered' **Trinidad, Puerto Rico, Jamaica, Guadeloupe** and the **Gulf of Mexico.**
Was finally sent back to Spain in chains after becoming very cruel as Governor General of New World and he died in 1506.
**Results:**
1 Columbus inspired people to explore further.
2 Europeans began to settle in the New World.
3 Without realising it, Columbus had discovered a new continent.

Amerigo Vespucci realised that the new lands were in fact part of a new continent. It is named after him: America. The **Treaty of Tordesillas** (1494) between Spain and Portugal drew an imaginary line down the Atlantic Ocean. All lands west of this line were to be Spanish while all to the east were to be Portuguese.

Ferdinand Magellan (1480-1521)
Portuguese sailor. Ships **Santiago, Victoria, Concepcion, San Antonio** and **Trinidad** – set sail on 20 September 1519.
Sailed along African coast and then down the South American coast. Lost *Santiago* and *San Antonio.*
Found passage through the **Magellan Straits** beside **Patagonia** and sailed into **Pacific Ocean.**
Arrived at islands that he named **The Philippines** after Prince Philip of Spain.
Magellan was killed on the island of **Mactan.**
The *Victoria* under **Sebastian del Cano** sailed the remainder of the journey and they arrived into Seville on 6 September 1522 to complete the first circumnavigation of the globe.

## The *Conquistadores*

Hernándo Cortés (1485-1547)
Spanish soldier who travelled into mainland America; discovered the Aztec civilisation and its capital **Tenochtitlan.**
King of Aztecs, **Montezuma** thought Cortés was a god called **Quetzalcoatl.** Spanish tried to steal gold and Aztecs threw Spanish out so Cortés conquered Aztecs and destroyed Tenochtitlan.
He was made Governor of New Spain and land was renamed **Mexico.**
Francisco Pizarro (1475-1541)
Spanish soldier who conquered the **Inca civilisation** and captured their leader **Atahualpa.**
Marched and defeated armies at capital of **Cuzco** and established a new capital at **Lima** and renamed the Inca empire **New Castile.**

## Results of Exploration

1. **Exploration continued:** North America, India, Middle East, Australia, Canada and Africa.
2. European countries became very **wealthy** due to their empires; from slavery, gold and silver.
3. New products like tobacco, pineapples, chocolate and potatoes were introduced to Europe.
4. Those countries facing out to the **Atlantic** gained in importance and those in the Mediterranean declined in importance.
5. **European culture** dominated native cultures. Spanish, Portuguese, French and English languages replaced native languages.
6. European diseases killed millions of natives, e.g. by end of sixteenth century almost all of Mexico's native population had died.
7. **Slavery** became a huge business as Europeans used natives to work on farms and in mines. It is thought that between 10-12 million African slaves were brought to America and Europe to work.

# 7 The Reformation – Revision Summary

## Causes of The Reformation (1517-1563)

1. Wealth of the Church
2. Influence of the Renaissance
3. Increasing power of the kings
4. Printing press and spread of ideas
5. Abuses of Church: **nepotism / simony/ absenteeism / pluralism**

## Martin Luther (1483-1546)

Born in Saxony; professor at Wittenberg – **Justification by Faith Alone;** 95 Theses; Papal Bull – excommunicated.
Diet of Worms 1521: Charles V – Edict of Worms
Kidnapped by Frederick the Wise of Saxony. Martin Luther writes Bible in vernacular.
Confession of Augsburg 1530.
Religious wars end with Peace of Augsburg: each prince to decide which denomination will apply in their local area.

## John Calvin (1509-1564)

Born in Noyon, France. Set up church in Geneva.
Wrote ***The Institutes of the Christian Religion*** (1537) – Predestination / Bible / two Sacraments.
Structure: Pastors / Teachers / Deacons / Elders.
Followers known as Calvinists, Presbyterians, Huguenots or Puritans.

## Henry VIII (1491-1547)

Henry VII > Henry VIII > Edward VI > Mary > Elizabeth I
Catherine of Aragon / Anne Boleyn / Jane Seymour
Act of Supremacy 1534 – Henry VIII becomes Head of Church
Act of Dissolution 1536 – Henry VIII takes all Church land in England
Edward VI – 42 Articles
Elizabeth I – Anglican Church / Act of Supremacy (1559) – Elizabeth I becomes Governor of Church.

## Counter-Reformation

**Council of Trent** 1545-1563, Trentino, Italy:
Gets rid of abuses / **Jesuits** (Ignatius de Loyola) / **Inquisition** – Spanish and Italian – Torture – auto-da-fé.

## Results of the Reformation

1. Conflicts and wars
2. Information / education / printing press
3. Increased power of kings / reduced power of Pope
4. New Christian Churches (denominations)
5. New alliances between countries

# 8 The Plantations – Revision Summary

Population of Ireland 1500

| | Gaelic Irish | Gaelicised Anglo-Normans | Old English |
|---|---|---|---|
| **Where they lived** | All over Ireland esp. rural | All over Ireland esp. urban | Pale and towns |
| **Religion** | Catholic | Catholic | Catholic |
| **Laws and customs** | Gaelic Customs | Gaelic (and English) Customs | English laws and Customs |
| **Examples of names** | O'Neill, O'Donnell, McCarthy | Fitzgerald, Burke, Butler | Barnwell, Fleming, Plunkett |
| **Relations with the English monarch** | Tension | Not trusted by English | Trusted by English |

**The Pale**
Area that stretched from **Dundalk–Kells–Trim–Clane–Tallaght–Dalkey.** Inside this defended area English customs and laws were used. English lived here. Regularly attacked by Irish.

## Reasons for Plantations

1. **Cost** of putting down rebellions was too high, e.g. Silken Thomas = plantations a better idea?
2. Cost of **War of the Roses** in England = give Irish land to soldiers.
3. **Spread of Protestantism** to Catholic Ireland.
4. Henry VIII wanted to **control Ireland** (announced he was king of Ireland in 1541).
5. Spanish were creating an **Empire** – English wanted one – start in Ireland.

**Surrender and Regrant**
Irish landowners would give their land to Henry VIII and in return he would give it back to them and an English Title, e.g. The O'Neill – Earl of Tyrone. Why?

- Irish leaders could ensure power/ land/ wealth stays with family and Henry VIII becomes king of Ireland.
- Ireland should then become loyal to crown and any rebels had land taken.

| Brehon Laws | English Patriarchal |
|---|---|
| Land owned by whole family | Eldest son gets everything. |
| Leader elected by whole family | Land stays from father to son. |
| New leader would be strongest person from family; sometimes led to great fights. | Increased wealth, power of one family. |

## Laois-Offaly Plantation (1556)

**Why?**
The **O'Moores and O'Connors** were stealing cattle and raiding Pale **(woodkernes).**
In 1553 Queen Mary took their land and invited planters because she wanted to:
1. **Protect** the Pale
2. **Control** native Irish population
3. **Spread** English laws.

**Plantation**
1. 160 land grants of up to 180 acres each to English and loyal Irish.
2. Use of **English language and customs.**
3. County towns of **Maryborough** (Portlaoise) & **Philipstown** (Daingean) established.
4. Laois changed to **Queen's county** and Offaly to **King's county.**
5. Sheriffs brought in to establish English Law.

**Success or Failure?**
Complete failure because:
1. Not enough people (English or Old Irish) wanted to take land.
2. Not enough English wanted to come to Ireland.
3. O'Moores and O'Connors continued to raid the Pale.

## Munster Plantation (1586)

**James Fitzmaurice Fitzgerald** – cousin of Earl of Desmond.
First rebellion (1569) failed but he goes and gets support from Pope as he sees it as a part of Counter Reformation.
Pope sends 600 troops – land at Smerwick Harbour 1580. Earl of Desmond joins rebellion and Lord Deputy Mountjoy surrounds rebels and they surrender – he massacres them!

**Results of Desmond Rebellions** (1569 and 1580)
1. Munster devastated – crops / cattle / land destroyed.
2. 30,000 died during rebellion.
3. Earl of Desmond beheaded – head sent to Elizabeth I and body hung in Cork.
4. All lands of Desmond confiscated.

**Munster Plantation** (1586)
1. Estates created of 4,000–12,000 acres.
2. Those who 'undertook' the king's rules/laws and were loyal were given land.

**Who were the Undertakers?**
Had to remove all Irish from land. Had to have approx. 90 English tenants, 71 household servants, craftsmen, e.g. carpenters/smiths etc., sheep, cattle and horses. Had to equip three horse-soldiers (tenants were required to equip one foot-soldier). Undertakers paid rents to the Crown.

**Problems**
1 By mid 1590s **only one-third of proposed number**s were planted or settled.
2 Had to **rent to Irish** because so few English willing to come to Ireland.
3 Constant **attacks** from Desmond sympathisers.
4 **Absenteeism** due to fear of attacks.

**Results**
1 **New towns** set up: Killarney, Lismore, Mallow.
2 New **farming methods** introduced.
3 A **Protestant minority** remained.

## Ulster Plantation (1610)

**Nine Years War, 1594-1603**
Elizabeth I and **Lord Deputy Fitzwilliam** encouraged **adventurers** to lay claims to land; imposition of sheriffs made Ulster chieftains uncomfortable.
Hugh O'Donnell had made an agreement with Papal Legate to defend Ulster from Protestantism.
Led by **Hugh O'Neill,** Earl of Tyrone, who had been educated in England and seemed to be loyal, and **Red Hugh O'Donnell.**
Defeated the English at **Battle of Yellow Ford** 1598 using **Gallowglasses** (foreign mercenaries from Scotland).
2,000 English troops died and whole country rises in support.
Spanish support and Philip II sends 4,000 troops to **Kinsale.** English navy and army surround them and so O'Neill and O'Donnell have to go and try to help them.
**Battle of Kinsale** Christmas Eve 1601. O'Neill loses. Signs **Treaty of Mellifont** in 1603 and regains rights and control over land but is constantly harassed by English. **Flight of the Earls.**

**Articles of Plantation**
1. **Undertakers:**
   Estates of 1,000 / 1,500 / 2,000 acres.
   Rent was very low to encourage undertakers.
   Expected to build stone house or castle.
   Undertakers located close to each other.
   Only have English or Scottish tenants.
   24 men over 18 years of age on an estate.
2. **Servitors** – largest group – allowed some Irish tenants.
3. **Loyal Irish** – located close to servitors (for security)
4. **London Craft Guild** – (Londonderry)

**Results**
1 Increase in **Protestant population:** 1640: 40,000 Scots out of 1 million.
2 **Religious** difference and tensions.
3 New **settlers firmly established** in Ulster and outnumbered Catholic Irish.
4 New **farming methods** introduced to Ulster: linen etc.
5 **New towns** established.

### Cromwellian Plantation (1652)

Tension in England between:
**Parliamentarians v Royalists = Oliver Cromwell/Roundheads v King Charles I/ Royalists.**
Civil war in England 1642; king beheaded in 1649 – Cromwell wins.

Ireland uses this opportunity to rebel in 1641 because:
1 **Angry** at previous plantations
2 Good time as **England is preoccupied with the civil war**
3 **Catholic response** to Protestantism.

Rising is <u>very</u> bloody with 2,000–10,000 planters killed; Catholic Irish set up the **Confederation of Kilkenny** in **1642** to organise Ireland.

Cromwell comes over to Ireland in 1649 with 12,000 Roundheads:
1 To **crush Catholic** rebellion.
2 To **punish rebels** and gain revenge for killing of Protestant planters.
3 To pay off **debts** to his soldiers for Civil War (in England) with land in Ireland.

Cromwell defeats the Catholics easily. Slaughter in Drogheda and other towns: he leaves soon after.

### Results of Cromwellian Plantation

1 **Act of Settlement** (1652)
  Rebels had all land confiscated.
  Those who couldn't prove loyalty – 'transplanted'– 'to hell or to Connacht'.
2 Land and economy of Ireland destroyed:
  Towns and farm land ruined.
  Catholic prisoners and priests sent to West Indies.
  30,000 soldiers go to Europe for work.
3 **Down Survey** (so-called because things were written 'down') by William Petty estimated that 11 million acres confiscated.
4 **Land in Protestant** hands:

| | Catholic ownership of land | Protestant ownership of land |
|---|---|---|
| 1600 | 90% | 10% |
| 1640 | 60% | 40% |
| 1700 | 15% | 85% |

# 9 Age of Revolutions – Revision Summary

### American Revolution

#### Background

**13 Colonies:** Virginia, Georgia, North and South Carolina, Maryland, Delaware, New Jersey, Pennsylvania, Philadelphia, New York, Connecticut, Massachusetts, New Hampshire. Owned by Britain, ruled by King George III.
**Seven Years War** between Britain (colonists and redcoats) v France. Britain wanted American colonists to pay for the war.

**Navigation Acts: Stamp/ Quartering/ Townshend Acts.** Colonists angry and create Sons of Liberty. No taxation without Representation – **Declaratory Act** – Britain has right to tax whoever they want. Colonists still angry – Boston Massacre (March 1770) 5 killed.
**Tea Act** – British East India Company receives exclusive rights for sale of tea in America.
**Boston Tea Party** (1773) – British furious – **Intolerable Acts** – First Continental Congress (1774).

**American War of Independence** (1774-1781)
Battles: **Lexington / Concord** – 2nd Continental Congress – Continental Army (led by George Washington) lose at **Bunker Hill.**
**4 July 1776 – Declaration of Independence** by **Thomas Jefferson**
Americans win at Boston but lose at **White Plains,** win at **Princeton** and **Trenton** but lose at Philadelphia – Congress have to leave Philadelphia. Americans win at Saratoga but spend winter at **Valley Forge** – bad times but Frederick von Steuben helps and French and Spanish send help. Washington finally defeats Cornwallis and British at **Yorktown.**
**Treaty of Versailles** (1783) – America gains independence.

**Results of American Revolution**
1 **Democracy** – Create Senate / House of Representatives / President (1st is Washington).
2 **Federal system** (each state makes its own laws but the country is run by central government)
3 **Individual rights** and **freedoms.**
4 Revolutionary **ideas** spread to Europe.

## French Revolution

**Causes**
**1 Louis XVI** (L16) had **absolute power** and Marie-Antoinette was extravagant and from **Austria**; hated by the people.
**2** Country divided: **Nobles and Church** – paid no taxes and lived well.
**3 Peasants** and middle class paid all taxes (e.g. gabelle/ taille/ tithe) and were very poor.
**4** Bad **harvests** meant price of bread etc. was very high.
**5** Country **bankrupt** from supporting America in war against Britain.
**6 Inspiration** from American Revolution for change.
**7** Middle class (bourgeoisie) wanted more power.
**8** Ideas of **individual freedom** from Rousseau, Voltaire.

**Events**
L16 calls on Estates General to raise more taxes.
- **First Estate: Clergy** (Bishops, cardinals etc. of Catholic Church).
- **Second Estate: Nobles** (Large landlords in chateaus – lords, dukes, marquis, etc.).
- **Third Estate: Bourgeoisie** (Tradesmen, lawyers – anyone who worked for their money).

1st and 2nd Estates join to force 3rd Estate to pay more tax – 3rd Estate refuses and takes **Tennis Court Oath** – that they would not stop until they got a fair deal.
L16 calls meeting of the **National Assembly** of 3 estates but fears he will lose power; L16 brings in troops; the sans-culottes and the poor of France **storm Bastille (14 July 1789)**
**Declaration of Rights of Man** (26 August 1789) – **liberty, equality, fraternity** / new **Flag** / Royal family move to Paris.

**Flight to Varennes** by Royal family, captured; **Constitution of 1791 – Constitutional Monarchy.**
France declares war on Austria – France ill-prepared. Sans-culottes storm palace and 21 January 1793 L16 beheaded and France declared a **Republic.** Britain and Netherlands also join war against France.
**Reign of Terror: Robespierre** and Jacobins set up Convention and then **Committee of Public Safety** to protect the Revolution: 40,000 people killed (mostly with guillotine). Eventually too many deaths and Robespierre executed on 28 July 1794.

**Results**

1 Emergence of **Napoleon Bonaparte.**
2 **Spread of ideas** of republicanism / liberty / equality / fraternity / democracy.
3 **Inspiration and assistance** to other revolutions around Europe, e.g. Ireland 1798.

## 1798 Rebellion & the United Irishmen

**Causes**

1 **Protestant ascendancy** – since plantations most land owned by Protestants.
2 **Penal Laws** – laws against Catholics and Presbyterians.
3 **Spread of ideas** from America and France.
4 Support and assistance from **France.**
5 **Middle class** (esp. Presbyterians) wanted more power.

**Events**

**Society of the United Irishmen** founded by **Wolfe Tone** (WT) and others on 18 October 1791.
Aims: **Separation** from England
**Violence** if necessary
**Unite all religions** together – **Catholic, Protestant (Anglican)** and **Dissenter (Presbyterian)**
1793 war broke out between France and England; United Irishmen made illegal; Wolfe Tone fled to America. WT then goes to France and gets 15,000 French troops to come to Ireland under **General Hoche.**
December 1796 French try to land in **Bantry Bay** but weather was too bad.
British government try to stop rebellion:

- **Spies** infiltrate United Irishmen.
- **Laws** passed to arrest members of illegal organisations and banned importation of guns.
- General Lake uses **torture** to disarm people; 6,000 weapons collected.
- Early 1798 British government **arrest main leaders** of United Irishmen; Lord Edward Fitzgerald escapes but is later killed in May 1798.

Rising starts anyway on **24 May 1798** when mail coaches are stopped leaving Dublin.

1. **Ulster:** High tensions due to secret societies; **Peep-o-Day boys and Defenders.** **Henry Joy McCracken** and **Henry Munroe** both try, but due to inexperience fail and are caught and hanged.
2. **Wexford:** Hatred between Catholics and Protestants; Led by **Bagenal Harvey** and **Fr. John Murphy,** Irish win at New Ross and Wexford. Catholics massacre hundreds of Protestants at Scullabogue and Wexford Bridge. British defeat Irish at Vinegar Hill.
3. **Mayo:** Aug 1798 French send 1,000 troops to Killala in Mayo under **General Humbert**. Defeated **General Lake** at Castlebar – Races of Castlebar – but eventually lost at Ballinamuck.
4. **Wolfe Tone:** WT arrives in Ireland October 1798 into Lough Swilly, Donegal. Captured by British and arrested. Tries to commit suicide in prison and dies a week later.

**Results**

1 **Act of Union** 1800: Britain takes direct control over Ireland – no longer a parliament in Dublin; people leave Dublin as city is not as important anymore.
2 Birth of **Irish Nationalism:** WT seen as the 'father' of violent (if necessary) nationalism.
3 **Constitutional Nationalists,** those who wished to achieve independent Ireland through peaceful means – **Daniel O'Connell** sought to gain vote for Catholics – **Catholic Emancipation.**
4 **Increased tension** between Catholics and Protestants in Ireland.
5 Rising of **Robert Emmet** 1803 (girlfriend – Sarah Curran).

# 10 Social Change in Britain and Ireland 1750-1850
## Revision Summary

### Social Change in Britain (1750-1850)

**Causes of Industrial Revolution in Britain**

1. Increase in population – more food available; improved medical knowledge (Edward Jenner's vaccination for smallpox).
2. Migration from countryside to cities due to changes in agriculture.
3. British access to raw materials from colonies.
4. Access to coal and iron which were plentiful in Britain.
5. British inventors.
6. New banks in Britain offered money and loans.

### Improvements in Agriculture

**1. Enclosure:** **(a)** Weeds and disease reduced
**(b)** New methods could be introduced
**(c)** Animals confined to fields.

**2. Inventors:** **(d) Charles 'Turnip' Townshend** – the Norfolk Crop Rotation system.
**(e) Robert Bakewell** – selective livestock breeding.
**(f) Jethro Tull** – seed drill.
**(g) Cyrus McCormick** – mechanical reaper.

**Results of Agricultural Revolution:**

1. More food produced and so food prices dropped.
2. Cheaper food available so population grew.
3. Large farmers became richer and farm labourers lost jobs (new methods) so became poorer.
4. Poor unemployed country people moved to cities to look for work.

### Industrial Developments

| **Textile Revolution** | | |
|---|---|---|
| **John Kay** | **Flying Shuttle** (1733) | weaving cloth on loom |
| **James Hargreaves** | **The Spinning Jenny** (1764) | spinning yarn |
| **Richard Arkwright** | The **Water Frame** (1769) | spinning yarn |
| **Samuel Crompton** | The **Spinning Mule** (1779) | spinning large amounts of yarn |
| **Edmund Cartwright** | The **Power Loom** (1785) | weaving large amounts of cloth |

| **Industrial Revolution Coal and Iron** | | |
|---|---|---|
| **Thomas Newcomen** | Steam engine (1712) | steam-powered engine |
| **James Watt** | Steam engine & fly wheel (1769) | more efficient steam engine |
| **Abraham Darby** | Smelting iron with coke (1709) | better, cheaper method of iron |
| **Henry Cort** | **Puddling and rolling** (1784) | better quality, reduced cost of iron |
| **Henry Bessemer** | **Bessemer Converter** (1856) | made iron into steel |

| Transport Revolution | |
|---|---|
| **James Brindley** | Designed the Bridgewater Canal into Manchester (1761) |
| **Thomas Telford** | Designed smoother and more durable roads (1803) |
| **John MacAdam** | Designed smoother and more durable roads (1800s) |
| **George Stevenson** | Adapted Watt's engine to create locomotive engine called The Rocket (1830) |
| **Isambard Kingdom Brunel** | Launched first large steam-powered ship across Atlantic called *The Great Eastern* (1860) |

## Society in Industrial Britain

Living conditions: slums: families lived in one room in a house, no toilets, no running water.
Health: life expectancy was low; diseases like **typhoid** and **cholera; smog** from smoke and fog – damp conditions caused **tuberculosis** – diseases spread quickly.
Working conditions: started at 5:30am and worked 12–16 hours, six days a week.
Factories: dangerous machines, wages low, children used in small spaces.
Mining: colliers dug seams of coal; children worked as trappers, hurriers. Dangers: explosions, flooding, Miner's Lung, bad backs from bending.
Leisure time: (Sundays off) – played sports such as rugby and football, went to bars and public houses.
Life of wealthy: lived in large houses, had servants, went to college and spent holidays at seaside.

**Improvements**

1. **Chartists:** in 1830s workers demanded right to vote, secret ballots, abolition of property requirement, salaries for MPs and annual parliamentary elections.
2. **Trade Unions:** were made legal in 1825 and in 1875 workers were allowed go on strike.
3. **Robert Owen:** set up new model factory village in New Lanark, Scotland.
4. **Lord Shaftesbury:** pushed for legislation for improvement in workers' rights.
5. **Factory Act 1833:** children under 9 could not work in factories and by 1842 children under 9 and women were not allowed to work in mines.

## The Irish Famine (1845–1848)

**Ireland in nineteenth Century**

Ireland ruled directly by British Parliament.
Ireland largely **agricultural (rural).**
Very few large towns – Belfast the only industrial city with ship-building and linen manufacturing.
Land was divided up into:
**Landlords** – some interested in tenants but many were **absentee landlords** living in Britain.
**Tenant** farmers – larger farmers were comfortable but most were subsistence farmers.
**Farm labourers** – cottiers rented small pieces of land **(conacre)** to grow potatoes.
Housing: wealthy lived in large houses but majority lived in small one-roomed mud huts.

## An Gorta Mór

**Causes**

1. Large population increase in nineteenth century: rose from 5 million at beginning of century to 8 million by 1841.
2. Very **little industrialisation** in Ireland; majority of people depended on farming so land was scarce.
3. Families became **dependent on potato** as it provided a high yield from a small amount of land and potatoes could be eaten throughout the winter.
4. New potato disease called **potato blight** was introduced in bird manure from South America and struck for the first time in 1845. Blight struck in 1845, 1846 and 1848. Potatoes were destroyed and

those that survived were eaten so that there was none to re-plant the next year.

5 The weakness of the population due to starvation meant that **diseases** such as typhus, the **relapsing fever, dysentry** and **scurvy** killed many.

**Government response**

1. British PM **Robert Peel** sent **Indian corn (maize)** to Ireland. Was known as **Peel's brimstone** as it was very difficult to cook.
2. **Public Works Schemes** set up to provide employment.
3. **Workhouses:** people could go to workhouses and get food and accommodation in return for work. Quaker (Society of Friends) **Soup kitchens:** offered free soup for the starving.

**Results**

1 **Evictions:** unable to pay their rent as they were starving, many tenants were evicted.

2 **Emigration:** without any hope in Ireland, many left Ireland. The ships were known as coffin ships as so many people died on board. About 1.2 million left Ireland between 1845 and 1851.

3 **Population decline:** with death and emigration the population dropped to 4.6 million in 1901 from 8 million in 1841.

4 **Politics:** many Irish were very angry at the British government's response and wanted to gain independence.

# 11 International Relations in Twentieth Century Europe

## Revision Summary

### World War I (1914-18)

**Background:** war between two groups:
**The Allies (the Entente Cordiale)** vs **The Central Powers**
Britain, France, Russia, Italy and USA vs Germany, the Austro-Hungarian Empire, Ottoman Empires and Bulgaria.

Allies defeated Central Powers in long war.
The Paris Peace Conference in 1919 was led by the leaders of Britain **(Lloyd George)**, the USA **(Woodrow Wilson)** and France **(Georges Clemenceau).**

- Americans wanted **14-Point Plan** that included self-determination for each country.
- French wanted revenge on, and compensation from, Germany.
- Britain wanted compensation from Germany and to reduce the size of German navy.
- Italy wanted: more land.

**Treaty of Versailles (1919)**

1 Germany had to accept the **War Guilt Clause** – accept all responsibility for war – and pay reparations.

2 Germany lost lots of land: Alsace-Lorraine to France; Silesia and Posen to Poland; Schleswig to Denmark.

3 Germany's army and navy were limited in size.

4 Germany not allowed to have troops in Rhineland beside France.

5 Ottoman and Austro-Hungarian Empires broken up into new countries.

6 League of Nations set up with aim of solving disagreements between countries.

**Results of WWI**

1 Resentment: Germany very angry at terms of Treaty. Disliked being blamed for war and paying large reparations. This anger was directed at those who surrendered and then signed the Treaty.
2 Unemployment and poverty: size of reparations, loss of land and failure of industries meant that unemployment and poverty rose.
3 New countries: many new countries were set up from the Ottoman, Austro-Hungarian and Russian Empires, e.g. Yugoslavia, Hungary, Poland and Finland.
4 Rise of the USA: the arrival of the USA into the war in 1917, and its involvement, meant it had become very powerful economically. After WWI the USA chose to follow a policy of isolationism.
5 League of Nations: Germany and Russia were not allowed join and the USA refused to attend so it was very weak.
6 Rise of **communism:** Russia's withdrawal from the war in 1917 was due to the success of **Lenin's** Bolshevik Party.

## Fascism in Italy

**Causes**

1 Treaty of Versailles: Italy had hoped for large amounts of land from the break-up of the Austro-Hungarian Empire. When they did not succeed, they stormed out of negotiations.
2 Memories of the past: Roman history and Roman ruins all around them.
3 Economics: Italy was heavily in debt after WWI, unemployment was high and prices were rising.
4 Democracy: many governments tried and failed to deal with problems in Italy and so people looked to extreme political parties like the Communists, while rich people feared this.

**Mussolini** founded Fascio di Combattimento in 1919 (also known as **Fascists**).
They believed in strong leadership, law and order, restoring Italy as a leading power, anti-Communist.
In 1922, Mussolini and his **Black Shirts** (fascist supporters) organised a **March on Rome** and forced King Victor Emmanuel to ask Mussolini to form a new government in October.

**Political policies**

Created **OVRA** (secret police).
**Acerbo Law** 1923: party with greatest number of votes would get two thirds of seats in parliament.
Censorship of press and removed king's ability to dismiss government ministers.
By 1926 he had banned all other political parties; full press censorship; becomes a dictator.

**Domestic policies**

Economy: **Corporate State** – government, employers and workers decide how to run areas of economy.
Built autostrada, drained Pontine Marshes, encouraged grain production; lowered unemployment.
Political opposition: OVRA and Blackshirts used violence and intimidation.
**Propaganda:** newspapers, radio and films showed Mussolini and fascists only in a positive light.
**Indoctrination:** schoolbooks and teachers had to be approved by fascists. After-school clubs taught young people to be good fascists and to love **Il Duce** (the Leader – Mussolini).
Religion: signed **Lateran Treaty,** 1929 with Pope which recognised Catholicism as the state religion.

**Foreign Policies**

1 Wanted to make Italy great again.
2 Forced Yugoslavia to give town of **Fiume** to Italy in 1924.
3 Against League of Nations objections, Italy invaded **Abyssinia** in 1935.
4 Supported Fascist Spanish leader **General Franco** in Spanish Civil War between 1936–1939.
5 In 1936 Italy and Germany formed an alliance – the **Rome-Berlin Axis.**

## Fascism in Germany

### Causes
1 Many in population resented Treaty of Versailles, the reparations and War Guilt Clause.
2 Blamed the **November Criminals** (politicians who signed Treaty of Versailles).
3 Economy: high unemployment and inflation, loss of land and colonies.
4 Politics: extremist politics especially Communists.

### Adolf Hitler
Born in Austria in 1889 and later fought for Germany in WWI.
After war, he worked as a spy for German government. Spied on National Socialist German Workers' (Nazi) Party but ended up joining them.

### Nazi Party
Pride in the German people and hatred for all non-German peoples – especially Jews.
Germany needed a strong leader to make Germany great.
The **Sturm Abteilung (SA)** also known as **Brown Shirts** used intimidation and violence.
The **Schutzstaffel (SS)** were created as Hitler's personal bodyguard.
Hitler took the name **Der Führer** (the leader).
Nazis liked marches, military rallies and one-armed salute. Used Swastika as their symbol.

Hitler tried to have a revolution but his **Munich Beer Hall Putsch** was unsuccessful and he was sent to prison where he wrote ***Mein Kampf*** (My Struggle):
1 German people were Aryans – a master race.
2 Germany should expand to include all German-speaking peoples.
3 To create space for the Aryans, Germany would expand east and create *lebensraum* (living space).
4 All non-Aryans, especially Jews and Gypsies, should be removed.
5 Communism should be destroyed.
6 Destruction of Treaty of Versailles.
7 Anti-Semitism (hatred of Jews).

### Growth of Nazism
Economy: **Wall Street Crash** in 1929 caused inflation and high unemployment.
Democracy: Many people disliked those politicians who signed Treaty of Versailles. Extreme parties on left and right made it difficult to create governments. Violence between communists and right-wing groups added to tension. Government unable to deal with economic problems.
Nazi party won majority in German Reichstag (parliament) in 1932.

### Domestic policies
- Created **Gestapo** (secret police) set up by Göering.
- Communist Party was banned in 1933 after the Reichstag was burnt down.
- **Enabling Act** 1933 allowed Hitler to pass any law without approval from parliament.
- Banned all non-Nazi trade unions and political parties and censored all media. Goebbels made Minister for Propaganda and National Enlightenment.
- Hitler took on position of President after death of President Hindenburg in 1934.
- In June 1934, **Night of the Long Knives** saw all the SA leaders and political opponents killed by SS. Any remaining opposition was sent to concentration camps.
- School books re-written and boys expected to join **Hitler Youth** and girls to join League of German Maidens. These groups were taught loyalty to Hitler and hatred of Jews.

### Economics
Created employment with large public works such as motorways.
New factories began to provide military materials and weapons.

New car for the people called the Volkswagen.
Married women paid to stay at home and have more children.

**Anti-Semitism**

- Jews were depicted in media as ugly and dirty. Boycotts of Jewish shops were organised. Jews were banned from government jobs.
- Nuremburg Laws 1935 tried to 'protect pure German blood' by banning Jews from voting, marrying German citizens and owning property.
- Jews were forced to wear Star of David on their clothes.
- Kristallnacht (Night of Broken Glass) November 1938 saw Jewish shops, businesses and synagogues burnt, 90 Jews killed, hundreds injured and thousands sent to concentration camps. Finally, to pay for the damage, the Jewish community was fined 20% of all their property.
- Jewish children banned from attending German schools.

## World War II (1939-45)

Hitler wanted to destroy Treaty of Versailles.
1936: German army marches into Rhineland.
Allies did nothing because:

1. France had built defence line (the Maginot Line) and needed British support to stop Hitler.
2. Britain had sympathy for Germany – believed Treaty of Versailles was unfair and saw Rhineland as domestic (German-French) issue. Their army was also unprepared for war; therefore they favoured appeasement.
3. The USA did not want to get involved in another European war.

Hitler signed the Rome-Berlin Axis with Mussolini and supported Franco in Spanish Civil War.
1938: Forced the **Anschluss** – the joining of Austria and Germany together.
At the **Munich Conference** it was agreed by Britain, France and Italy to let Germany occupy Sudetenland in Czechoslovakia.
1939: Hitler then invaded the rest of Czechoslovakia.
Hitler and Stalin signed the **Nazi-Soviet Non-Aggression Pact** – neither would attack the other – and agreed to divide Poland between them.
Germany invaded Poland, using **Blitzkrieg** (lightning war) – very fast and effective. German airforce (Luftwaffe) bombed all major roads, bridges. German tanks (Panzer) divisions destroyed any defences. Infantry (Wehrmacht) finished off any resistance. Soviet troops also invaded Poland in September.

3 September 1939 – war declared on Germany by France and Britain.
**The Allies:** Britain and France; USA and USSR (both joined in 1941); China (invaded by Japan in 1937)
**The Axis Powers:** Germany, Italy and Japan (invaded China in 1937); Hungary (joined in 1940) Romania (joined in 1941).

1940: **Phoney War:** 1939-40 when nothing happened as Allies were preparing for war and building up military strength.
April: Germany invaded Denmark and Norway.
May: Germany invaded Holland, Luxembourg and Belgium thus avoiding French Maginot Line
British sent 250,000 men in British Expeditionary Force but they had to retreat to **Dunkirk** where they were rescued by hundreds of private boats which sailed across the English Channel.
June: France surrenders and is divided into two: the north is occupied by Germany and Vichy France in the south is loyal to Germany.
Sept: Germany launches **Operation Eagle** and **Operation Sealion**:
Eagle: Plan to defeat the **British Royal Air Force** and the bombing of Britain's defences by Luftwaffe (this period was known by the British as the **Battle of Britain**). The bombing of London was known as the Blitz.

Sealion: Plan to invade Britain by sea once the defences had been destroyed by Luftwaffe. Hitler finally gives up his plans to invade Britain in September 1941 after losing too many planes in the Battle of Britain.

Battle of the Atlantic: Hitler used German **U-Boats** (submarines) to sink British ships.
Italy invaded Yugoslavia and Greece but ran into trouble and had to ask for German help.

1941: After huge success by German forces throughout Europe and Africa, the Russian winter causes problems for Germany and the attack on Pearl Harbour brings America into the war.
April: German-Italian victory in Yugoslavia and Greece.
June: **Operation Barbarossa:** German Northern army attacked Leningrad. Centre army attacked Moscow. Southern army was to secure oil and wheatfields of Ukraine.
Dec: German advance had got within 32 kilometres of Moscow, were besieging Leningrad and had reached Stalingrad. Now they had to stop as the Russian winter froze oil/fuel in vehicles and poorly equipped soldiers froze to death. The Soviet army (scorched earth policy) had destroyed all food and supplies so supplies were running low. When the Germans stopped, the Soviet General Zhukov launched a counter-attack.
On 7 December, the Japanese attacked the American naval base at **Pearl Harbour** and destroyed 8 battleships and 13 other ships. American President Theodore Roosevelt declared war on Japan and therefore Germany declared war on America.

1942: 3 major battles begin to turn the tide against Axis Powers: Stalingrad, El Alamein and Midway.
1. **Stalingrad:** Germans under General Paulus are at the gates of Stalingrad. Stalin told the Soviet army not to surrender. The Germans were forced to fight hand-to-hand through the streets of the city and by October were exhausted.
   In November, Soviet counter offensive (Operation Uranus) trapped 290,000 German soldiers in the city. The Germans fought until January 1943 when German **General Paulus** surrendered.
2. **El Alamein:** The German Afrika Corps under **Rommel** had pushed to El Alamein. **British General Montgomery** managed to halt the German offensive and fought them at El Alamein. Rommel retreated and American troops under General Eisenhower landed in the west. Rommel was caught in a pincer and 275,000 German and Italian troops surrendered in May 1943.
3. **Midway:** Sea battle between American and Japanese fleets resulted in an unexpected victory for the Americans. The loss of so many ships meant that Japan was unable to hold the islands it had conquered.

1943: Throughout 1943, British and American troops landed and invaded Italy.
The Soviet army continued to push the Wehrmacht westward.
Nov: The leaders of the USSR, the USA and Britain met in Tehran to discuss the invasion of Europe planned for June 1944 known as Deliverance Day (D-Day).

1944:
June: 120,000 allied troops supported by 20,000 paratroopers landed along French coast of Normandy.
Aug: Over one million Allied troops had landed in Europe and Paris had been liberated.
Dec 1944 – February 1945: the last offensive by Hitler called the Battle of the Bulge stopped the Allied push to Berlin for a short time.

1945:
April: Hitler committed suicide and General Admiral Karl Doenitz agreed to an unconditional surrender on 7 May. The next day was known as Victory in Europe (VE) Day.
Aug: Two atom bombs were dropped: one on **Hiroshima** killing between 60-70,000 people and three days later a second killed 40,000 in **Nagasaki.**
Japan surrendered on 14 August and it was known as Victory in Japan (VJ) Day.

**How did Allies win?**

1 Sheer numbers of soldiers and resources when the USA and the USSR joined the war.
2 Germans reliant on inferior armies like those of Italy meant they had to divert troops away from fronts.
3 Unwise military decisions of Hitler, e.g. not allowing Paulus to retreat from Stalingrad.

**The Holocaust**

- Anti-Semitism was part of Nazism and as Nazi Germany expanded, it attempted to exterminate all Jews living in these countries. Jews were forced to live in areas of cities called ghettos. In 1941 the Einsatzgruppen was formed to exterminate all Jews within USSR.
- Concentration camps set up throughout Germany for Jews and enemies of the Nazi state. Prisoners were forced to work and treated very badly.
- 1942 **Adolf Eichmann** was put in charge of 'Final Solution'– the extermination of the entire Jewish community.
- Extermination Camps were set up in Poland and western USSR (e.g. **Auschwitz/Birkenau/ Sobribor/Treblinka**). Jews were gassed to death and cremated.
- It is thought that up to 6 million Jews died in the Holocaust.
- Many Roma, Gypsies, those with physical or mental disabilities and homosexuals were also sent to extermination camps. It is thought about 200,000 Roma were killed.
- While some people helped protect Jews living in Nazi-controlled lands, many ignored the issue for fear of the Nazis or due to anti-Semitism.

**Results of World War II**

1 Loss of life: estimated 55 million people were killed. Of the 55 million, 20 million were from the USSR.
2 Destruction of Europe: most of Europe lay in ruins. Cities, roads, railways and industries had been destroyed. The USA offered Marshall Aid after the war to help rebuild Europe.
3 End of European power: The European countries were no longer as powerful. The USA and the USSR were now the main economic and political leaders.
4 Europe divided: The USSR controlled most of the eastern half of Europe and installed Communist governments. The western half of Europe was still democratic and capitalist.
5 The Cold War: the ideological divide between the USSR and the USA increased the tensions between the countries and led to the Cold War.
6 European Unity: European leaders tried to cooperate more to avoid future conflict.
7 The United Nations: after the failure of the League of Nations, a new organisation was set up in New York called the United Nations (UN).

# 12 Ireland in the Twentieth Century – Revision Summary

## Ireland in 1900

**Nationalists**

Ireland (apart from Ulster) – was agricultural, Catholic, pro-Irish independence.
**Irish Parliamentary Party IPP** (**John Redmond**) wanted Home Rule: a parliament for Ireland in Dublin with power over Irish affairs.

**Unionists**

North-East Ulster, Industrialist, Protestant, pro-Britain.
**Ulster Unionist Party** (**Edward Carson** and **James Craig**).
Unionists against Home Rule because:

1 Might lose out on ship-building, linen, rope manufacturing trade with Britain.
2 Catholics of South would dominate – 'Home Rule meant Rome Rule'.
1910 Election gives IPP balance of power in Westminster; Home Rule seems certain in 1914

**Unionists' reaction:**
Solemn League and Covenant (400,000 sign)
Ulster Volunteer Force (UVF) – 100,000 members; get 24,600 rifles and 3 million rounds of ammunition into Larne 1914.

**Nationalist reaction:**
Irish National Volunteers – 160,000 members; get 900 rifles and 25,000 rounds of ammunition into Howth.
The Great War breaks out and Home Rule is shelved till after war.
Ulster Volunteers go to Great War.
Redmond goes with National Volunteers to fight.
**Eoin MacNeill** creates Irish Volunteers who stay in Ireland and refuse to fight in war.

## Irish Social Life

- **Gaelic Athletic Association** (GAA) set up 1884 by **Michael Cusack** and **Maurice Davin** to promote hurling/ football/ handball. Help establish clubs throughout Ireland.
- **Gaelic League** set up in 1893 to halt decline of Irish language.
  **Eoin MacNeill** and **Douglas Hyde** establish newspaper ***An Claidheamh Solais*** (Sword of Light).
  Sent teachers throughout Ireland to teach language.
  St. Patrick's Day as holiday. Cultural festivals, e.g. the annual Oireachtas.
- **Anglo-Irish Literary revival: WB Yeats** and **Lady Gregory** set up Abbey Theatre 1903.
- **1913 Lock-Out:**
  ITGWU set up by **Jim Larkin** to improve wages and conditions.
  **William Martin Murphy** owned Dublin United Tramways Company/ Easons/ Irish Independent/ Clerys: was against trade unions and refused to let employees join.
  **Irish Citizen Army** and **Irish Labour Party** set up by **James Connolly** to protect workers.
  Strike called but workers eventually gave up.

## 1916 Rising

**Build-up to Rising:**
**Irish Republican Brotherhood** (IRB) (secret organisation which infiltrated other organisations). Used forged Castle Document to get MacNeill's Irish Volunteers to join rebellion but he later realised it was a forgery.
Connolly and Irish Citizen Army join.
Roger Casement sent to Germany to get arms: caught on *Aud* ship and arrested.
Rising postponed to Easter Monday; blood sacrifice.

The Rising
Proclamation read out on Sackville Street by Pádraig Pearse.
Key locations taken by rebels (GPO/ Bolands Mills/ College of Surgeons).
Soon more British troops arrive.
Gun-ship *Helga* shells GPO from Liffey.
By Saturday the rebels surrender.

**Results:**
**1.** Public against Rising at first, but after execution of leaders their attitude changes.
**2.** British and Irish believe it was **Sinn Féin** (SF) that led Rising; **Arthur Griffith** leader of SF, arrested.
**3.** Public support SF and want full independence. SF promise to create new Irish parliament.
**4.** British threaten conscription - SF anti-conscription.
**5.** 1918 General Election: SF won 73 seats and IPP only 7 seats.
**6.** 21 January 1919 - first meeting of **Dáil Éireann.**
**7.** SF creates new government and declares independence.
**8.** Irish Volunteers now known as Irish Republican Army under Michael Collins.

## War of Independence 1919-1921

21 January 1919 - Soloheadbeg, County Tipperary - 2 Royal Irish Constabulary killed by IRA; Beginning of War of Independence.

**Combatants:**

Irish:

1 IRA under Collins. 2 Flying Columns used guerrilla warfare. 3 'The Squad' killed any informers.

The British

1. Royal Irish Constabulary – policemen.
2. Black and Tans: ex-soldiers from WW1 who wore khaki and RIC jackets of black or dark green and tan-coloured trousers.
3. Auxiliaries: ex-army officers; by 1920, over 40,000 British army and police forces in Ireland.

**Main events:**

1. SF Lord Mayor of Cork, Terence MacSwiney arrested and imprisoned in Britain. Hunger strike – he died after 73 days.
2. **The Squad kill** 11 British secret service men.
3. **Bloody Sunday** (Sunday 21 November 1920). **Black and Tans** retaliate by shooting into match at Croke Park killing civilians.
4. Black and Tans burn Cork city centre down in retaliation for ambush by Flying Column.
5. Truce agreed 11 July 1921 – 2,000 British forces (including RIC) and 752 IRA men killed.

**Negotiations** led by Collins without de Valera

Irish wanted: 1 Full independence. 2 A 32-county Ireland.

British wanted: 1 Ireland within Commonwealth. 2 Partition of Ireland.

**Results of the Treaty:**

1. Southern Ireland now Irish Free State – not a republic.
2. Remains within the British Commonwealth and all TDs must swear oath of allegiance to King of England.
3. British retain naval ports of Lough Swilly / Queenstown (Cobh) and Berehaven.
4. Northern Ireland remains within UK.
5. Boundary Commission to decide on border.

**Reactions in Ireland:**

**Arguments For Treaty**

**1** More freedom than under Home Rule.

**2** Ireland has freedom to gain independence.

**3** IRA had no more resources to fight.

**Arguments Against Treaty**

**1** Not free when king is head of state.

**2** Not loyal to Republic if must swear oath.

**3** Not a full 32-county Ireland.

Dáil vote on 7 January 1921: For the Treaty: 64 votes: Against: 57 votes.

**1922 General Election:**

Pro-Treaty SF: 58 seats. Anti-Treaty SF: 35 seats. Other candidates (all pro-Treaty): 35 seats.

## Irish Civil War 1922-1923

**Pro-Treaty:** Irish Free State Army (Regulars) – Collins.

**Anti-Treaty:** (Irregulars) - De Valera / Rory O'Connor / Harry Boland.

Main events:

1. O'Connor took Four Courts and Collins shelled it. After two days the Irregulars surrendered on 5 July.
2. Limerick captured 20 July and Cork fell to Free State on 12 August. Griffith died 12 August.
3. 22 August Michael Collins killed at Béal na mBláth.

4. Special Powers Act 1922 allowed Irregulars to be arrested, tried and executed.
5. Ceasfire called in May 1923.

**Results:**
1. 927 killed including 77 executed and 12,000 anti-Treaty soldiers in prison.
2. Divided country and the Treaty still divides Ireland's politics.
3. Millions of euro in damage to cities, roads and railways.

# 13 International Relations 1945-2000 – Revision Summary

### Emergence of the Superpowers

Introduction:
After WW2, two countries emerged as the main powers in the world: The USSR and the USA.
Both had won the war.
Both had large natural resources like coal, iron and oil.
Both had very large populations.
Both had strong economies that recovered from WW2 very quickly.

### Differences: USA v USSR

| | USA | USSR |
|---|---|---|
| Ideology | Capitalism | Communism |
| Economics | Free trade and private ownership | State-controlled economy: state-owned property |
| Elections | Multi-party free elections | One-party elections |

**Legacy of WW2:**
- After WW2, both countries wanted to spread their influence in the countries of Europe: USSR in the east and the USA in the west.
- USSR wanted to create a 'buffer-zone' of friendly countries to protect it from Germany. The countries occupied had puppet governments installed and fell into the Soviet sphere of influence.

**Truman Doctrine:**
American President Harry Truman supported any country that would fight against communism. This Truman Doctrine of containment of the communist threat was the basis for American foreign policy.
**The Atomic Bomb:**
After the USA had dropped their bombs on Hiroshima and Nagasaki, the USSR was determined to develop its own bombs and tested its first in 1949.
**Marshall Aid:**
The money given to European countries to rebuild their economies was known as Marshall Aid after the US Secretary of State George Marshall. Stalin forced all Eastern European countries to refuse the Aid. Instead, the Communist Information Bureau organised the countries in Eastern Europe.

Conflict between two superpowers that was not actually a battle but **Cold War.**

## The Berlin Blockade (1948-49)

**Causes:**

Germany divided into 4 zones: American, British, French and Soviet.
Berlin was in Soviet zone but was also divided into 4 zones.
A new currency, the Deutschmark, was introduced but USSR refused to let it be used in their zone.

**The Berlin Blockade:**

USSR blocked all road and rail links into Berlin.
The western allies began **Operation Vittles** which airlifted millions of tonnes of food and supplies into Berlin.
Airlift went on for 11 months before Soviet government ended the blockade.

**Results:**

1 USA, Britain and France unified their western sectors into Federal Republic of Germany while the USSR established the German Democratic Republic in the east.
2 The economic differences between west and east Germany meant people began to escape to the west. The borders were closed but people continued to do this in Berlin. The east German government built the Berlin Wall in 1961 to prevent any more people escaping.
3 In 1949, a military alliance called the **North Atlantic Treaty Organisation (NATO)** was set up to prevent the spread of communism. It included most western European counties and the USA. In retaliation, the USSR set up the **Warsaw Pact Alliance** between all the communist countries in the east.

## The Korean War 1950-1953

**Causes:**

After WW2, Japan withdrew from Korea and the USSR occupied the north and the USA occupied the south.
Two countries were created: the Communist People's Republic of Korea in the north led by **Kim Il Sung** and the Republic of Korea in the south led by **Syngman Rhee.**

**The War:**

- With the support of Stalin, Kim Il Sung invaded the south in 1950.
- American President Harry Truman asked the UN to support an invasion to oppose the north.
- As USSR and China were not part of the UN Security Council, the UN agreed to send General Douglas MacArthur and a multinational UN force to Korea.
- The UN attack pushed the North Koreans almost as far as China.
- Mao Tse-Tung of China responded by sending 300,000 troops into North Korea.
- MacArthur proposed a nuclear attack on China but Truman refused and dismissed MacArthur.
- The negotiations for a truce lasted two years until the death of Stalin. An armistice was signed in July 1953.

**Results:**

1 Continued hostility between North and South Korea
2 America saw their policy of containment as a success.
3 UN was seen to be prepared to intervene.

## The Cuban Missile Crisis 1962

**Causes:**

1. In 1959, communist rebels overthrew corrupt dictatorship in Cuba. Led by **Fidel Castro,** a communist government was installed.
2. The USA did not like having a communist country so close to its borders and so Cuba turned to the USSR for military and economic help.
3. In 1961, the Americans supported an unsuccessful invasion of Cuba at the Bay of Pigs. Castro now looked to **Nikita Khrushchev,** the Soviet leader, to help protect Cuba from invasion.

**The Crisis:**

- In 1962, the USSR began to construct missile sites in Cuba that were capable of attacking American cities at short notice.
- After seeing photographs of the missile sites from American spy planes, the American President, **John F Kennedy,** demanded their removal. Khrushchev refused.
- JFK announced a blockade of Cuba to prevent Soviet ships and supplies from landing in Cuba.
- As the Soviet ships arrived in Cuba, the world feared the outbreak of nuclear war.
- Khrushchev finally backed down and a deal was done:
  1 The USSR would withdraw its missiles from Cuba.
  2 The USA would promise not to invade Cuba.
  3 The USA would withdraw its missiles in Turkey.

**Results:**

1 Cooperation between USA and USSR improved.
2 A hotline between the two leaders was created.
3 A Test Ban Treaty was signed banning testing of nuclear weapons on land or sea.

**Other areas of conflict:**

The USA in Vietnam.
The USSR in Afghanistan.
The USSR crushed uprisings in Hungary and other Eastern European countries.
Both countries tried to build more weapons in the arms race.

**Reform of the USSR**

The Soviet leader, Mikhail Gorbachev (elected 1985), began reforms of the USSR:

1. Economic reforms called **perestroika.**
2. Political reforms on censorship and political dissent called **glasnost.**
3. Signed numerous treaties to reduce military spending in arms race.
4. Borders of Eastern Europe and the west were opened. Berlin Wall was torn down.
5. Free and democratic elections in Eastern Europe permitted.
6. Some Soviet Republics like the Baltic States declared independence from the USSR.

## European Cooperation

**Causes:**

1 After WW2, European leaders realised it was better to cooperate.
2 Desire to spread human rights and democracy throughout Europe to avoid political extremism.
3 To improve economic conditions of people of Europe.

**Early Cooperation:**

1. The Benelux Union: Belgium/ Netherlands/ Luxemburg cooperated on economic and taxation issues.
2. The Organisation for European Economic Cooperation (OEEC) set up to distribute money from Marshall Aid.

3. Council of Europe: set up by 10 countries including Ireland to discuss cooperation.
4. The European Coal and Steel Community (ECSC): Germany/ France/ Italy and Benelux to cooperate in the areas of coal and steel production.

**The European Economic Community**
March 1957, the Treaty of Rome was signed by the six members of the ECSC and created the European Economic Community (EEC):
1 Customs duties between these countries abolished.
2 Common market of goods, services, money and people was created.
3 The Common Agricultural Policy (CAP) was created to provide a guaranteed price for farming produce.
4 European Social Fund created to help the poorer areas of the EEC.

**Structures:**
**The European Commission:** made up of appointees of member states (commissioners). They draft proposals for the Council of Ministers and the European Parliament.
**The Council of Ministers:** made up of national ministers for specific areas of responsibilities e.g. agriculture or foreign affairs.
**The Parliament:** directly elected representatives from each country depending on its size of population.
**Court of Justice:** ensures all members states abide by the European laws.
**Court of Auditors:** checks that all funds are spent legally and correctly.

**Expansion and integration of the EEC:**
1. Ireland, Britain and Denmark all joined in 1973. Since then the community has expanded to 27 member states.
2. The **European Monetary System** was introduced in 1979. This linked member state currencies to each other.
3. **Single European Act 1986:** integrated the member states further and changed the name of the EEC to the European Community.
4. The **Maastricht Treaty 1991:** came into force in 1993: (a) The EC was renamed the European Union (EU). (b) Closer political ties were agreed. (c) A new currency called the Euro was introduced. (d) Social Charter
5. **Common Foreign and Security Policy (CFSP)** introduced to create a common agreed policy on these issues.
6. **Amsterdam Treaty 1997:** strengthened laws on employment and discrimination and prepared EU for further expansion to the east.

**Criticism of EU:**
- The EU does not represent the views of the public well enough. This democratic deficit should be overcome by giving greater power to the Parliament.
- Fears of increased military capability of the EU, i.e. might see it involving itself in future wars or conflicts.
- Smaller countries can be dominated by their larger, more powerful neighbours.

**Results of European Cooperation:**
1 Peace within borders of EU
2 Democracy and human rights have been strengthened
3 EU is far wealthier and economically more powerful as a cooperating bloc.
4 The Social Fund has helped poorer areas of Europe.
5 CAP has maintained and benefited farming communities in Europe.

# 14 Ireland since 1948 – Revision Summary

### Coalition Government 1948-1951

Taoiseach: **John A Costello** of **Fine Gael** with **Clann na Poblachta** and the **Labour Party.**

Achievements:
**1** 1949 Established Ireland as a Republic
**2** Refused to join North Atlantic Treaty Organisation (NATO); continued to be neutral.
**3** Elimination of Tuberculosis (TB). **Noel Browne** of Clann na Poblachta was Minister for Health. TB killed 2,000-4,000 people every year; Browne set up a programme to get rid of it – very successful.

**Mother and Child Scheme**
Set up to provide free health care for all women and children but Catholic Church and doctors opposed it as it would give women too much independence. Costello dropped the idea and Browne resigned with all Clann na Poblachta TDs. End of government and general election 1951.

### Fianna Fáil 1951-1954

Taoiseach: **De Valera. Fianna Fáil** formed government with help of Independent TDs including Noel Browne.
Problems:
**1** Balance of Payments Crisis: Ireland importing more than it exported to Britain.
**2** Unemployment after WW2.
**3** Emigration to UK and US: 197,000 in 1951-1956 and 212,000 in 1956-1961.

### Inter-Party Government 1954-1957

Taoiseach: John A Costello of Fine Gael with Clann na Poblachta and the Labour Party.
Same problems as previous government.

### Fianna Fáil 1957-1973

In 1957 election Fianna Fáil won a majority. In 1959 de Valera resigns as Taoiseach and becomes President. **Seán Lemass** becomes Taoiseach in 1959.
1 New Programme for Economic Expansion by **T.K. Whitaker,** Secretary of Dept. of Finance.
- Grants for farmers and business to produce more.
- Foreign industry encouraged to come to Ireland to create jobs with grants and tax breaks.
- Shannon Town and Industrial estate established.
- Emigration falls and population increases.

**2** Education: Minister **Donogh O'Malley** (from 1966): Free secondary education; Free school transport; Grants for building schools; Comprehensive schools and RTCs established.
**3** Introduction of Telefís Éireann (RTÉ).
**4** Second Vatican Council of Catholic Church; church becomes more liberal.
**5** Irish people started to travel to Europe on holidays i.e. establishment of Aer Lingus.

## Ireland in the 1970s

| Elections | Government | Taoiseach |
|---|---|---|
| 1973 | Fine Gael and Labour | Liam Cosgrave |
| 1977 | Fianna Fáil | Jack Lynch 1977-1979,<br>Charles Haughey 1979-1981 |

| | | | |
|---|---|---|---|
| 1981 | | Fine Gael and Labour | Garret FitzGerald |
| 1982 | | Fianna Fáil | Charles Haughey |
| 1982 | | Fine Gael and Labour | Garret FitzGerald |
| 1987 | | Fianna Fáil | Charles Haughey |
| 1989 | | Fianna Fáil | Charles Haughey 1989-1992<br>Albert Reynolds 1992 |
| 1992 | 1992-1994 | Fianna Fáil and Labour | Albert Reynolds |
| | 1994-1997 | Fine Gael, Labour & DL | John Bruton |
| 1997 | | Fianna Fáil and Progressive Democrats | Bertie Ahern |

**Achievements:**
1. Joins EEC in 1973
2. CAP/ Structural Funds and Social Fund/ Common market all help economy.
3. Loss of fishing rights and cheaper imports.
4. Sunningdale Agreement 1973 (Lynch and British PM Edward Heath)
5. Power-sharing government in Northern Ireland
6. Council of Ireland
7. Loyalists (Ian Paisley) go on strike and power-sharing collapses.

**Problems:**
1. International Oil Crisis: 1973–1974.
2. Inflation / unemployment/ emigration.
3. Budget deficit
4. Arms Trial (1970) Haughey/ Blaney accused of importing arms.
5. Dublin and Monaghan Bombings (1974) 33 killed and 300 injured.

## Ireland in the 1980s

**Achievements:**
1. Anglo-Irish (Hillsborough) Agreement (1985).
2. Gives Republic a say in running of Northern Ireland.

**Problems:**
1. Economic difficulties:
2. Budget deficit leads to cuts in spending on education and health
3. Unemployment
4. Emigration to USA and UK
5. Numerous governments during 1980s.

## Ireland in 1990s

**Celtic Tiger:**

Social Partnership (Government/ Trade Unions and Employers); low wage increases.

Foreign computer companies attracted to Ireland due to low taxes, English speaking, educated workforce, inside EU etc.

Economy grows faster than any other European country.

Full employment and low emigration.

**Problems:**
1 Overheated housing market
2 Unregulated banking sector
3 Rising inflation.

# 15 Northern Ireland – Revision Summary

## Northern Ireland 1920-1960

Government of Ireland Act 1920 created state of Northern Ireland.
Made up of counties: Antrim/ Armagh/ Derry/ Down/ Fermanagh/ Tyrone.
Northern Ireland remained part of United Kingdom.
Parliament at Stormont was dominated by the mainly Protestant Ulster Unionist Party led by James Craig.

**Unionist Control of power**

The police force called the Royal Ulster Constabulary (RUC) and the part-time reserve force called the B-Specials were set up. Both were almost exclusively Protestant and often discriminated against Catholics and nationalists especially as sectarian violence erupted in 1921-1922.

- **Special Powers Act 1922** allowed government to imprison suspects without trial (internment). This was used against the nationalist community.
- **Voting systems:** Government replaced the proportional representation (PR) system of voting with 'first-past-the-post' system. This favoured the larger parties such as the Ulster Unionist Party.
- **Gerrymandering:** this was the system whereby the constituency borders were changed to ensure that UUP candidates were elected even in areas where nationalists were in the majority.
- **Sectarianism:** Protestants were often given preference for jobs by local authorities. This meant that Catholics were generally poorer than their Protestant neighbours.

**World War II**

- Harland and Wolff shipyard and Shorts plane manufacturing created employment during war.
- Linen industry also benefited – making uniforms and parachutes.
- American soldiers in Northern Ireland between 1942 and 1945 provided an economic boom.
- Roads and ports were improved to help the distribution of the amount of goods going through Northern Ireland.
- By the end of WW2, unemployment dropped to just 5%.
- Bombing by Luftwaffe in 1941 killed 745 people and destroyed 3,000 homes.

**Welfare State**

National Health Service offered free healthcare to all.
Education Act 1947 gave free secondary education to all.
Better pensions and unemployment assistance provided.
Unionists want to stay in UK and Catholics were given a better education.

## 1960-1973: Tensions Rise

Terence O'Neill became PM of Northern Ireland in 1963 and invited Irish Taoiseach Seán Lemass to Northern Ireland. This caused problems in extreme Unionist areas.

Northern Ireland Civil Rights Association (NICRA) set up with aims:

1. Equality for Catholics in voting, housing, education and jobs.
2. Abolition of Special Powers Act 1922 and disbanding of the B-Specials.
3. End of gerrymandering.

They hoped to achieve these aims through peaceful means such as organised marches. In 1968 a civil rights march was banned and when it went ahead anyway, it was forcefully dispersed by the RUC.

**Battle of the Bogside:**

In the Catholic area of the Bogside in Derry, Catholics barricaded their neighbourhood. When the Protestant Apprentice Boys marched through Derry, riots broke out. 7 died and 3,500 people were driven from their homes (3,000 were Catholic). British Army sent into Northern Ireland to control situation in 1969.

**Political changes:**

- **Catholic/Nationalist:**
  John Hume and Austin Currie set up Social Democratic and Labour Party (SDLP).
  IRA split in 1969: Official IRA moved away from violence and Provisional IRA continued with violence.
- **Protestant/Unionist:**
  Ian Paisley created the Democratic Unionist Party (DUP).
  Ulster Volunteer Force (UVF) re-established and the Ulster Defence Association (UDA) established.
  Internment introduced by NI government 1971: NICRA objected as it was aimed at Catholics and Nationalists.

- **Bloody Sunday (30 January 1972)**
  13 unarmed civil rights marchers in Derry were killed by British Army. This resulted in increased support for IRA and increased violence. Stormont was suspended and direct rule from London introduced.

## Road to Peace (1973-2000)

**Sunningdale Agreement 1973**
Power-sharing between UUP and SDLP.
Council of Ireland set up to give more southern influence in Northern Ireland affairs.
The Agreement was destroyed by extreme unionists (loyalists) and the Ulster Worker's Council's strike (1974) when all water and electricity was shut down.

**Hunger Strikes 1981**
IRA prisoners demanded political prisoner status. Bobby Sands and others began hunger strike to gain this status. British PM Margaret Thatcher refused to negotiate and 10 hunger strikers died. Increased support for IRA.

**Anglo-Irish (Hillsborough) Agreement 1985**
Agreement between the British and Irish governments:
1 The Republic of Ireland had a say in the running of Northern Ireland.
2 There would be no change to status of Northern Ireland without consent of majority of population.

**Downing Street Declaration 1993**
Statement from British and Irish governments stating that Britain had no economic or strategic reason for remaining in Northern Ireland and that self-determination was only way that status could change.

**The Good Friday Agreement 1998**
Created Northern Ireland Assembly: a power-sharing parliament in Northern Ireland.
Republic would remove articles 2 and 3 (claiming jurisdiction over NI) from Constitution.
Referenda in Northern Ireland and the Republic whether or not to accept Agreement: accepted by large majorities in both parts of Ireland.

# 16 Ireland: Social History – Revision Summary

## Rural Life

### Early century

- Rich landlord had large houses and lived on estates. Majority were Protestant and saw themselves as British.
- Wealthy farmer: owned approximately 50-300 acres and lived in large, two-storey houses.
- Small farmer: 40% rural dwellers lived on 15 acres or less. Had thatched houses with small windows. Toilets were outside.
- Farm Labourer: approximately 260,000 farm labourers in Ireland in 1901. Small cottages had thatched roofs, two rooms and a loft.
- Running water from outside well or pump.
- No electricity.
- Most people depended on agriculture.
- Farm work done manually and used horse-drawn machinery.

### Changes

- Electrical Supply Board (ESB) set up in 1927 and led to the electrification of homes.
- Agricultural Credit Corporation (ACC) set up to provide loans for farm improvements.
- Electrical washing machines, television, central heating and modern appliances made life easier.
- Rural homes now modern bungalows with slate roofs.
- Membership of EEC in 1973 helped provide funds for farmers, especially the CAP and the Social Policy grants.
- Many moved away from small tillage to livestock.
- Tractors, combined harvesters and other new methods made farming more efficient.

## Urban Life

### Early century

- Beginning of century only 32% lived in cities.
- Dublin had 350,000, Cork had 76,000 and Limerick had 40,000 people.
- Wealthy people lived in large townhouses while poor people lived in tenements where whole families lived in a single room.
- 22.9% of Dublin's population lived in one-bedroom tenements, mostly without electricity.
- Life expectancy was under 50 and child mortality was twice that of London.
- Toilets were outside and diseases such as cholera and TB were common.
- Belfast was the only city with heavy industry (Harland and Wolff and linen manufacturing).
- Stout manufacturing and distilling offered some employment in Dublin (Guinness and Jameson) and Cork (Murphy's and Power's).

### Changes

- From 1930s the government began building corporation houses in the suburbs for tenement dwellers.
- Between 1926 and 1946, the number of families living in homes of one or two rooms in Cork, Dublin or Limerick fell from 39% to 23%.
- Urban Regeneration Projects in the last decades of the century have helped develop inner-city locations.
- More foreign industries were encouraged to set up in Ireland from 1960s onwards. These were located on the outskirts of cities.
- Large industrial parks and shopping centres were built in the suburbs of cities.
- Between 1923 and 1996, the % of people working in agriculture fell from 53% to 10% while those working in services grew from 34% to 63%.

## Sports and Leisure

### Early century

- GAA was popular throughout Ireland while rugby and soccer were more popular in the cities. Many rugby and soccer clubs were established during this time.
- 10,000 people watched the 1911 All-Ireland hurling final.
- Many theatres were established at the end of the nineteenth century and beginning of the twentieth (The Gaiety and Abbey Theatres, the Cork Opera House).
- The first cinema opened in 1909 in Dublin.
- In 1926, Ireland's first radio station, 2RN, began broadcasting – offering music, sports programmes and news.

### Changes

- During the 1960s, showbands who performed at dancehalls became popular.
- Discos grew during the 1970s and in the 1990s electronic music played by DJs became fashionable.
- RTÉ television began to broadcast in the 1960s and chat shows such as *The Late Late Show* or soap operas such as *The Riordans* were widely watched.
- Videos and later DVDs allowed people to watch films at home.
- Game-consoles allowed players to play against each other over the internet.
- Holidays abroad especially in Spain and Portugal became very common in the late 1970s and 1980s.
- The GAA, rugby, soccer, athletics, golf, boxing and cycling have grown in popularity and Ireland has enjoyed huge success internationally through its sportsmen and sportswomen.
- By 1995, almost €900 million a year was being spent on sport in Ireland.

## Transport

### Early Century

- Transport was slow and the most common method was on foot.
- Roads were no more than dirt tracks while cobblestones were used in cities.
- Electric trams were used to travel in the cities of Belfast, Cork and Dublin.
- Longer distances were travelled by trains. This method was slow as trains stopped at every station.
- Cars were very rare: there were only 7,845 licensed cars in Ireland in 1945.
- Ships travelled to Britain, Europe and America from Kingstown (Dun Laoghaire), Queenstown (Cobh) and Belfast.

### Changes

- In the 1960s, trams in the cities were replaced by buses.
- Motorways were built throughout Ireland linking cities together – especially since joining the EEC.
- By the end of the century 4 out of 5 households had one or more cars.
- Trainlines closed down as people began to drive more.
- In 2004, on-street trams, Luas, were reintroduced in Dublin.
- Ferries linking Ireland to Britain and Europe have become faster and more comfortable.
- Air travel increased in the 1990s with the arrival of cheaper flights.

## Communications

### Early century

- Letter-writing was the main method of communication. In cities there were three daily postal deliveries.
- The telegraph was another method and it was faster and it was possible to send a telegram across the world very quickly. This method was possible due to Morse code.
- Telephones were rare and it was necessary to contact an operator at a manual telephone exchange who would then connect your call.

### Changes

- From the 1960s, phones became common in private homes. By the 1990s, the mobile phone was introduced. By 2000, one-third of the population had a mobile phone.
- Facsimiles were used in the 1990s but have been largely replaced by email.
- By the end of the century almost half of homes had internet access.
- Skype, social networking sites, Twitter and email have ensured that communication is cheaper, faster and easier than ever before.

## Role of Women

### Early century

- **The Intermediate Education Act,** 1878 and the **Royal University of Ireland Act,** 1879 allowed women to sit exams and take university degrees but it was not until 1904 that Trinity College allowed women onto the campus and 1908 until all other universities followed suit.
- **The Dublin Women's Suffrage Association** and the **Irish Women's Franchise League** were established to fight for the vote for women. The IWFL was set up by **Hanna Sheehy-Skeffington.** These women were known as suffragettes. By 1918, women over 30 were given the vote.
- In 1922 the **Constitution of Ireland** gave women and men over the age of 21 the right to vote.
- One third of all employed women worked in domestic service and 45% of all National School teachers were women.
- In 1932, de Valera passed the **Marriage Ban** that forced women to give up their jobs in the public service and as teachers when they got married.
- The **Conditions of Employment Act,** 1935 gave the government the right to limit the number of women working in any industry.
- The 1937 Constitution supported the traditional view of women by recognising their 'special role' within the home.
- By 1946 only 2.5% of married women were employed compared to 25% in England. Over one third more women than men emigrated between 1946-1951.

### Changes

- The **National Council of Women** and the **Irish Women Workers' Union** helped to improve women's position in society.
- The Commission on the Status of Women issued a report in 1972 and recommended 49 ways to eradicate inequality.
- The marriage ban was lifted and in 1977 the **Employment Equality Act** banned any form of gender discrimination.
- Girls now outperform boys in school in almost every subject.
- There have been two female Presidents (Mary Robinson 1990-1997, and Mary McAleese 1997- ) and the first female Tánaiste (Mary Harney) was appointed in 1997.
- There is still a lot of discrimination and gender inequality in Irish society.

# Notes

# Notes

# Notes

# Notes

## Notes